—— PRAISE FOR ——

The Ultimate Cognitive Behavioral Therapy W...

"When we're looking for relief from overwhelming emotions such as anxiety or anger, we need more than sound advice—we need specific tools that help us *act* on what we know. This workbook offers both excellent grounding in CBT and practical steps for applying these powerful principles in everyday life. If you're ready to make lasting changes for the better, I strongly recommend *The Ultimate Cognitive Behavioral Therapy Workbook*."

–Seth J. Gillihan, PhD, author of *The CBT Deck* and *Mindful Cognitive Behavioral Therapy*

"Drs. Leslie Sokol and Marci Fox have indeed created the ultimate CBT workbook! It includes dozens of useful handouts for working through challenges with self-doubt, depression, anxiety, anger, urges, and more. The structured approach and clear language used by the authors help simplify the science of working with these complicated issues, and the written exercises provide the tools and practice necessary to manifest these principles in daily life. Highly recommended for both therapists and their clients!"

–Richard Sears, PsyD, ABPP, author of the *Cognitive Behavioral Therapy & Mindfulness Toolbox* and *ACT with Anxiety*

"Drs. Sokol and Fox's latest book, *The Ultimate Cognitive Behavioral Therapy Workbook*, is a wonderful contribution to the field. It's both comprehensive in scope and highly practical for clinicians of all experience levels. The authors review the essential theoretical foundations underlying CBT and follow this up with highly applicable interventions for a variety of conditions, including depression, anxiety, anger, and urge control. There are a number of practical worksheets that can be readily applied with your clients. I learned a lot from reading this book, and I am confident you will too."

–David M. Pratt, PhD, MSW, author of the *CBT Toolbox for Depressed, Anxious & Suicidal Children & Adolescents* and the *Advanced CBT Toolbox for Depressed, Anxious & Traumatized Youth*

"*The Ultimate Cognitive Behavioral Therapy Workbook* is an invaluable resource for people wanting to learn how to deal with a variety of life's challenges, either as a standalone resource or to accompany treatment. The exercises are clear and based on the best empirical science. It should be a major boon to anyone who wants to improve the quality of their life."

–Steve Hollon, PhD, Gertrude Conaway Vanderbilt Professor of Psychology

"We know that many people who are struggling with clinical symptoms and everyday life problems are not getting the therapy or support they need. Sokol and Fox's *Ultimate Cognitive Behavioral Therapy Workbook* brings together core evidence-based tools and techniques that would be used in therapy and makes them accessible to everyone. Written in a warm and relatable tone, this workbook would be great for anyone who is interested in CBT but does not have access to enough (or any) traditional therapy. It would also be a helpful companion for clients in therapy who want to continue to strengthen their coping skills and translate what they are learning into real life change. Because such a wide variety of clinical issues and problems are discussed, this is a resource that will be returned to time and time again."

–Elena Welsh, PhD, author of *Trauma Survivors' Strategies for Healing* and *The Panic Deck*

"Sokol and Fox have done it again! While some CBT workbooks are somewhat narrow in focus (dealing with one disorder or condition), *The Ultimate Cognitive Behavioral Therapy Workbook* covers a range of emotional and behavioral issues and is written in an engaging, organized, lucid, and reader-friendly style. The way in which each exercise is organized into learning, practice, and coping reminder skills is innovative and helpful; complex CBT concepts and interventions are translated into user-friendly language and guidelines; and CBT-based skills for a variety of different problems are demonstrated with numerous examples and worksheets to facilitate practice."

–**John Ludgate, PhD,** founding fellow of the Academy of Cognitive Therapy and psychologist
    at the CBT Center of Western North Carolina

"Drs. Sokol and Fox's *The Ultimate Cognitive Behavioral Therapy Workbook* is an approachable self-help text that translates the principles of CBT to consumers. It is also an excellent adjunct to therapy, providing clients with a 'read along' as a resource to their treatment. The authors explain the basics of CBT and how that theory is applied in a clear, practical, and straightforward manner, with illustrations and worksheets showing how those precepts can be applied to the more common problems that this therapeutic approach can effectively address."

–**Cheryl Carmin, PhD,** director of clinical psychology training at The Ohio State University

"Leslie Sokol and Marci Fox—two highly accomplished and experienced CBT therapists, trainers, and authors— have again succeeded in writing an excellent and practical volume for anyone interested in improving the psychological quality of their life. *The Ultimate Cognitive Behavioral Therapy Workbook* is a thorough yet concise collection of cognitive behavioral self-assessments and self-help exercises that can be used by readers whether they are actively in treatment or not. Sokol and Fox cover a broad swath of clinical concerns with empathy, conceptual understanding, and know-how born of decades of practice. This is a wonderful new resource that will provide therapists with a practical, effective tool and that will further the personal wellness of any readers interested in applying CBT to their lives."

–**Cory F. Newman, PhD,** director of the Center for Cognitive Therapy and professor of psychology
    in psychiatry at the Perelman School of Medicine at the University of Pennsylvania, author of *Core
    Competencies in Cognitive-Behavioral Therapy*

The Ultimate
COGNITIVE BEHAVIORAL THERAPY
WORKBOOK

50+ Self-Guided CBT Worksheets to Overcome Depression, Anxiety, Worry, Anger, Substance Use, Other Problematic Urges, and More

Leslie Sokol, PhD and Marci G. Fox, PhD

Published by
PESI Publishing, Inc.
3839 White Ave
Eau Claire, WI 54703

Cover Design: Amy Rubenzer & Emily Dyer
Editing: Jenessa Jackson, PhD
Layout: Emily Dyer

ISBN: 9781683735649 (print)
ISBN: 9781683735656 (epub)
ISBN: 9781683735663 (epdf)

PESI Publishing
pesipublishing.com

DEDICATION

To Aaron T. Beck, MD
Our cherished, missed, and beloved inspiration

CONTENTS

INTRODUCTION

Several years ago, we wrote ***The Comprehensive Clinician's Guide to Cognitive Behavioral Therapy***, which we created as a go-to resource for therapists to understand and apply the principles of CBT. Feedback from individuals who bought the *Comprehensive Clinician's Guide* told us how helpful the exercises and worksheets were, but they were looking for more to help clients bridge the gap from the therapy office to real life. This made us realize that we needed to do more. Inspired by our desire to continue helping others, we decided to write this step-by-step workbook, which takes our previous book one step further by helping clients put their skills into action.

Just like anything in life, acquiring a skill requires practice. It is not enough to have knowledge or insight if we don't use it to feel better or take effective action. The practice begins in your therapy session, but you can only apply it to real life by practicing outside of the office. This book was written to give you, the client, an opportunity to do just that. It provides you with the tools needed to act as your own therapist, helping you succeed in your journey toward self-growth and empowerment.

WHAT IS IN THIS BOOK

The Ultimate Cognitive Behavioral Therapy Workbook offers a unique, structured, and experiential approach to overcoming a variety of clinical issues and everyday problems, including depression, anxiety, worry, panic, anger, impulsivity, and substance abuse. We wrote it to help you understand how your thinking patterns, emotions, and actions work together—and how these processes can sometimes keep you stuck and prevent you from moving forward. Grounded within the basic principles of CBT, it is filled with practical exercises and worksheets that will help you restructure your thinking, face your fears, curb your anger, resist unhelpful urges, and grow the most positive and accurate view of yourself. Instead of letting negative thoughts drive unnecessary distress and engaging in unhelpful behaviors that thwart your ability to achieve your goals, you will learn to think in a more accurate, positive, and helpful way and choose more effective behaviors.

Not only does this book arm you with tools to overcome your difficulties, but it also contains a variety of confidence-boosting exercises intended to help you squash any doubts that are preventing you from moving forward. When you feel confident under pressure, you can face situations with courage and more effectively deal with outside pressures from your home, work, family, and social life. Confidence is at the core of eliminating all psychological distress. It provides you with a foundation of wellness so that happiness is no longer in the shadows.

Within each exercise, you'll find three unique sets of tools to help you strengthen your CBT skills: *learning*, *practice*, and *coping reminders* tools. The learning tool summarizes the main takeaways of each exercise, whereas the practice tool provides you with additional ideas to apply the skill being taught in your day-to-day life. Finally, the coping reminders tool provides short and simple affirmations that will empower you to keep moving on your journey to wellness.

WHOM IS THIS BOOK FOR?

This self-guided workbook is designed to help general readers like you better understand themselves, their distress, and their difficulties. You can use it in conjunction with a chosen therapist or as a stand-alone guide to manage life's challenges. This workbook can also be used by mental health professionals who are looking to equip their clients with the tools they need to become their own CBT therapist outside of the therapy room.

Regardless of your reasons for picking up this book, we are confident that *The Ultimate Cognitive Behavioral Therapy Workbook* lays out a clear path that will guide you along your journey to lifelong well-being. Think of it as your champion and ally—always at your side rooting for your success and happiness. Knowing that you have this resource in your corner, you'll be equipped to face any challenges that life throws your way.

Although making changes may seem daunting, it is possible! We see it daily in our work. By reading through this workbook and using the worksheets in your everyday life, you'll have an opportunity to practice the fundamental skills of wellness until they become more natural over time. Try them out! Run it as an experiment. You can learn how to retrain your thinking so that you can reclaim feelings of happiness, build a strong and empowering sense of self, and take positive actions to reach your goals.

⬡1
COGNITIVE MODEL

THE COGNITIVE MODEL

The cognitive model, which is the cornerstone of CBT, provides a way for us to understand why we react the way we do when we are faced with a situation, event, or experience. According to the cognitive model, when we are confronted with a particular situation, we have an automatic thought about that situation, which then triggers us to react with certain emotions, behaviors, and physiological sensations.[1] That means that situations in and of themselves do not cause distress. Rather, it is how we *perceive* or *interpret* those situations that drive distress and determine how we react and respond. The following diagram is a visual representation of the basic cognitive model.

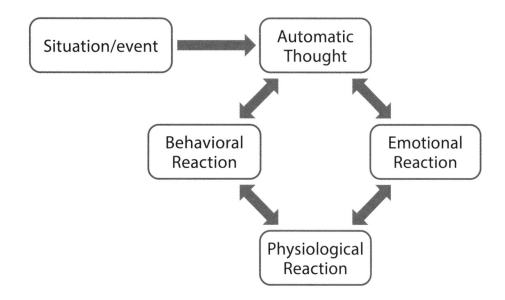

To understand how this works in practice, let's say that late one evening, you get an email from your boss asking to meet tomorrow (situation/event). In response, you think to yourself, "This isn't good! He must not be satisfied with my work performance" (automatic thought). Because you think your boss must want to meet about something unfortunate, you begin feeling anxious (emotional reaction), your stomach starts turning in knots (physiological reaction), and you decide to grab a beer from the refrigerator to quell your nerves (behavioral reaction). As you can see from this example, it's not the email itself that causes you to feel and act this way, but how you *interpret* the email.

---

1 Beck, A. T. (1964). Thinking and depression II. Theory and therapy. *Archives of General Psychiatry, 10*(6), 561–571. https://doi.org/10.1001/archpsyc.1964.01720240015003.

In understanding how to apply the cognitive model to your own self-help journey, here's what you should know:

- Situations do not cause distress.

- Situations don't make you feel or act a certain way.

- Your interpretation of the situation—that is, what you think about it—drives your emotional, physiological, and behavioral reactions.

- Just because you think something does not mean that it is true.

- Feelings, although important, aren't facts.

- Physiological reactions, or body responses, can arise when you misinterpret the situation, and they don't necessarily reflect something bad.

- You can examine your own thinking.

- You can learn to recognize when your thoughts are true and when they are false, exaggerated, or unhelpful.

- You can learn to dump untrue thoughts and replace them with more helpful accurate thoughts.

The worksheets in this chapter will provide step-by-step guidance in teaching you how to systematically examine your thinking and connect your thoughts to your emotions, body responses, and behaviors.

CAPTURE YOUR THINKING

• • • • • •

Your thoughts and emotions are connected. That means that the content of your thoughts shapes the content of your emotions. For example, imagine that someone you live with has just returned home, ignores you, and disappears out of sight. What might you be thinking? Here are some possible thoughts: "How rude! They should have said hello and checked in," "Oh no! Something is wrong! They might be in trouble," "They really don't like me," or "I guess they really have to go to the bathroom." Reflecting on each of these thoughts, how do they make you feel? It is likely that each thought triggered a different feeling: anger, anxiety, sadness, or neutrality, respectively.

Therefore, the first step in taking control of your emotions and overcoming distress is to start learning how to pay attention to your thoughts. This worksheet provides an opportunity for you to do just that. Think back to when you last remember feeling one or all of these emotions—sad, anxious, angry—and try to identify what you were thinking at the time. Some examples are provided for you first, followed by spaces for you to fill in your own responses.

Feeling: Sad   Thought: I will never get what I want.

Feeling: Anxious   Thought: I am going to catch Covid and die.

Feeling: Angry   Thought: They should have texted me back.

YOUR TURN:

Feeling: _____ Thought: _____

Feeling: _____ Thought: _____

Feeling: _____ Thought: _____

Feeling: _____ Thought: _____

Feeling: _____ Thought: _____

Feeling: _____ Thought: _____

Notice that the content of your emotion is directly related to the content of your thought.

LEARNING

Our thoughts influence our feelings.

....

 PRACTICE

Every time you notice yourself feeling a strong emotion this week, try to capture the thought that accompanies it. Keep a log to see if you notice any familiar patterns of thoughts.

....

 COPING REMINDER

- You don't need to let your emotions run your life.
- You can change the way you feel by changing the way you think—and capturing your thoughts is the first step.

CONSIDER ALTERNATE VIEWPOINTS

• • • • • •

As you've learned, we experience distress as a result of the way we *interpret* a situation, as opposed to the situation itself. However, we don't always interpret the world clearly, and we can instead jump to conclusions, ignore information, or fail to consider more reasonable points of view. Therefore, the second step in taking charge of how you feel, after paying attention to your thoughts, involves learning to see the situation from different viewpoints. For example, let's return to the example at the start of this chapter—where your boss emailed you asking to meet the next day. Instead of imagining the worst-case scenario (e.g., your boss wants to fire you), you could consider what an alternative viewpoint might be (e.g., your boss wants to congratulate you for your hard work). You may be inclined to doubt this alternate viewpoint at first, as your original thought might seem more realistic to you. But remember, just because you think something does not necessarily mean that it is true. You can still consider these alternate viewpoints as possibilities.

The way you think shapes how you feel and behave. While you may interpret situations correctly sometimes, other times it can lead to distress when you're looking at the situation in biased, inaccurate ways. To gain control of your feelings, you need to practice looking at situations from different perspectives, as if you were a person on the outside looking in. This way, you can learn to see things more accurately.

In this exercise, you'll have an opportunity to look at the same situation from two different perspectives—a distressing one versus neutral one—to see how your interpretation impacts your emotions, body reactions, and behavior. An example is provided for you first, followed by spaces for you to fill in your own responses.

EXAMPLE:

Situation: Your friend doesn't text you back.

Distressing interpretation:

Thought: They should have texted me back by now!

Emotion: Angry

Body reaction: Clenched fists, muscle tension

Behavior: Repeatedly check the phone

Alternative interpretation:

Thought: They are probably busy and not paying attention to their phone.

Emotion: Neutral

Body reaction: Calm

Behavior: Wait patiently or find another way to reach them

YOUR TURN:

Situation: Your friend cancels your dinner plans at the last minute with a vague reason.

Distressing interpretation:

Thought: _____

Emotion: _____

Body reaction: _____

Behavior: _____

Alternative interpretation:

Thought: _____

Emotion: _____

Body reaction: _____

Behavior: _____

Situation: Your partner asks to have a serious conversation after dinner.

Distressing interpretation:

Thought: _____

Emotion: _____

Body reaction: _____

Behavior: _____

Alternative interpretation:

Thought: _____

Emotion: _____

Body reaction: _____

Behavior: _____

LEARNING

The way you interpret a situation influences your feelings, body reactions, and behaviors. Your interpretations about this situation may be valid, completely invalid, or somewhere in between.

PRACTICE

The next time a situation upsets you, ask what you are telling yourself about the situation. Think of what a friend or another trusted person might say, and consider a more helpful or accurate viewpoint to guide your behavior.

COPING REMINDER

• You can reduce your distress by looking at the situation through another viewpoint.

• Take a few steps back to get a more positive and accurate view.

• Adjust your lens before believing what you're seeing.

LINK YOUR THOUGHTS, FEELINGS, AND ACTIONS

• • • • • •

The cognitive model is not linear, meaning that a change in any one variable impacts the others. Therefore, changing the way you think can change the way you feel, physiologically respond, and behave. Similarly, changing your behavior can influence how you feel, think, and physiologically respond. Finally, changes in your physiology can also affect how you feel, behave, and think.

While changing your behavior can provide the impetus to change your distress, it may only result in temporary relief rather than enduring improvement. That's because when you change your behaviors, it provides you with a temporary distraction from the things that bother you, but as soon as you are no longer distracted, the problem remains. Behavioral change is most effective when it provides the necessary data for new learning to take place—that is, for cognitive change to occur. Research has shown that enacting this cognitive change is the most effective intervention point. Therefore, it is helpful to do both—modify thinking and behavior—in order to see the most lasting changes.

Use this worksheet to see the connection between your thoughts, feelings, and behaviors in response to a situation—and see how changing your thoughts or behaviors affects your distress. The next time you feel distressed, return to this worksheet and describe the situation, including how you are thinking, feeling, behaving, and responding at the time. Then try changing your thoughts or your behavior to see what happens. An example is provided for you first, followed by spaces for you to fill in your own responses.

EXAMPLE:

Situation: I am lying in bed feeling tired and unmotivated, and I don't feel like doing anything.

What are you thinking? I can't do anything. I am a waste.

What are you feeling? Discouraged

How are you behaving? Continuing to lie in bed

How is your body responding? I feel sleepy.

Option 1: Modify the behavior

Behavior: Physically force myself to get out of bed and brush my teeth, put on some clothes, make breakfast, and do one task from my to-do list

Emotion: Less discouraged

Thought: I guess I can get something done, maybe I am not a waste.

Body reaction: I feel energized.

Option 2: Modify the thought

Thought: I have been tired and felt like not doing anything before, and yet when I force myself to act, I can. I can just get out of bed and do something.

Emotion: Less discouraged

Behavior: Get out of bed

Body reaction: I feel rejuvenated.

YOUR TURN:

Situation: _____

What are you thinking? _____

What are you feeling? _____

How are you behaving? _____

How is your body responding? _____

Option 1: Modify the behavior

Behavior: _____

Emotion: _____

Thought: _____

Body reaction: _____

Option 2: Modify the thought

Thought: _____

Emotion: _____

Behavior: _____

Body reaction: _____

LEARNING

Changing your behavior or thinking can change how you feel.

....

PRACTICE

Over the course of the next week, pay attention to any times you are in distress or behaving ineffectively. Then try changing your thinking or behavior to see what happens.

....

COPING REMINDER

- You have power over how you feel by changing how you think and what you do.

- You can reduce your distress.

②
COGNITIVE CONCEPTUALIZATION: UNDERSTANDING YOU

THE ROADMAP OF YOU

Do you ever wonder why you react the way you do? We all react differently to situations and events, and how *you* react is influenced by the underlying beliefs you have about yourself. Specifically, when a situation happens to you—and you develop subsequent automatic thoughts about that situation—those thoughts don't develop out of thin air. Rather, they arise from a set of core beliefs that you hold about yourself as a person, which have developed throughout your entire life starting from when you were very young. When these core beliefs are characterized by self-doubt, it can lead you to interpret situations from a negative lens—causing you to react in distressing ways.

Self-doubt typically revolves around two themes: desirability or competency. When you doubt your desirability, you might think of yourself as unattractive, unlikeable, bad, unwanted, or unworthy. When you doubt your competence, you may think of yourself as a failure, inadequate, helpless, useless, or incapable. This chapter will help you uncover the self-doubt lurking inside of you. You'll learn to identify your doubt labels, which are the nasty names you call yourself when your insecurity takes over. Once you identify your doubt labels, you can learn to question them so that your faulty beliefs aren't always getting in the way and causing you to needlessly overreact.

WHAT YOU VALUE

In order to identify the core beliefs that underlie your thoughts, feelings, and behaviors, it is important to first understand your personality style and what you value. That's because personality falls along a continuum of sociotropy and autonomy. People with a sociotropic personality value interpersonal relationships over everything else; they desire to be liked, accepted, valued, and desired. In contrast, people with an autonomous personality value achievement, mobility, and independence. They desire to be thought of as competent, capable, and strong.

Your biological nature, in combination with the environment you grew up in, contributes to the development of these values. For example, were you a baby who liked to be held all the time? A kid who always wanted to hang out with your friends? As an adult, do you tend to place greater value on social activities (e.g., attending a wedding or birthday celebration) over performance-related activities (e.g., doing work assignments, taking an exercise class)? If so, you may lean toward sociotropy. In contrast, if you have a more autonomous personality, you might have slept soundly alone in your crib as a baby, have preferred to engage in your own hobbies rather than having fun with a friend, and may currently prioritize work or other personal tasks over social invitations.

Where we sit on this continuum can shift over time, sometimes becoming more extreme or landing in the middle. Major life events—such as getting married, having children or grandchildren, getting our first job, or moving—can pull us along the continuum in one direction or the other. Some people also teeter between the two personality styles, falling somewhere in the middle of the continuum, although they may tilt in one direction or the other. Which are you?

ARE YOU MORE SOCIALLY ORIENTED?

· · · · · ·

To determine the extent to which you lean toward a more sociotropic personality style, read through the following statements and indicate whether or not they apply to you.

1. T or F Being loved or accepted feels better to me than accomplishing a task.

2. T or F I believe it's more important to be viewed as nice than smart.

3. T or F I care about what other people think of me.

4. T or F I tend to pick what others want to do over what I want to do.

5. T or F It's more important for me to be liked than to do what seems right for me.

6. T or F I find it easier to go with the flow than to assert my preferences.

7. T or F I don't like competition and am likely to fall apart under pressure to compete.

8. T or F I am more likely to be concerned about what others think when I choose my clothes, cut my hair, or act in public.

9. T or F My goals are easily swayed by the influences of others.

10. T or F My self-worth comes from my social success.

11. T or F I would compromise what I want to do to be with my friends.

12. T or F I would turn down a work opportunity to be there for a friend or loved one.

LEARNING

The more statements you endorsed as true, the more sociotropic your personality is. To determine whether you are extremely, moderately, or mildly sociotropic, tally up the number of items you marked true:

Mildly sociotropic	0–2
Moderately sociotropic	3–6
Extremely sociotropic	7–12

 PRACTICE

Whenever you find yourself having to decide between a social invitation and a work responsibility, pay attention to the choice you make. If you tend to accept more social events, it validates your sociotropic personality style.

 COPING REMINDER

- There are no judgments when it comes to your personality style.
- Being sociotropic in nature is neither good nor bad, just true.

ARE YOU MORE ACHIEVEMENT ORIENTED?

• • • • • •

To determine the extent to which you lean toward a more autonomous personality style, read through the following statements and indicate whether or not they apply to you.

1. T or F   I set goals and strive to reach them.

2. T or F   My self-worth comes from my performance in school, athletics, and extracurricular activities, or from doing what I want to do.

3. T or F   If I must choose between doing what I want to do or taking up an opportunity to be social, I typically choose what I want to do.

4. T or F   I prefer to be considered capable or smart rather than nice or friendly.

5. T or F   I take my social life for granted and place more importance on working hard to succeed or on doing what I want.

6. T or F   I define myself by what I do and not by how much people like me.

7. T or F   I thrive on competition.

8. T or F   I usually don't make decisions, like which clothes to wear or how to cut my hair, with others' opinions in mind.

9. T or F   I would turn down a social invitation for work or something I wanted to do instead.

10. T or F   I make achievement or income my priority.

11. T or F   I enjoy doing what I like even if no one does it with me.

12. T or F   My self-worth comes from my achievements.

LEARNING

The more statements you endorsed as true, the more autonomous your personality is. To determine whether you are extremely, moderately, or mildly autonomous, tally up the number of items you marked true:

Mildly autonomous	0–2
Moderately autonomous	3–6
Extremely autonomous	7–12

 PRACTICE

Whenever you find yourself having to decide between a social invitation and a work responsibility or choosing to do what you would prefer, pay attention to the choice you make. If you tend to place values on your achievements (or on doing what *you* want to do), it validates your autonomous personality style.

 COPING REMINDER

- There are no judgments when it comes to your personality style.
- Being autonomous in nature is neither good nor bad, just true.

UNDERSTAND YOUR VULNERABILITY

It is important to better understand your personality style—and how it affects what you value in life—because when your values are compromised or thwarted, it is likely to activate self-doubt. For example, when someone with a sociotropic personality experiences any degree of social conflict, it activates their underlying self-doubt beliefs, but someone with an autonomous personality will experience self-doubt when their performance or independence is threatened. This self-doubt is what makes you more vulnerable to distress.

The following are examples of events that can bother socially oriented people:

- Disagreeing with others

- Feeling rejected or insulted, whether real or imagined

- Being left out or not included

- Having someone upset with them

- Feeling awkward in social situations

- Not being called or texted back

- Being judged or insulted, especially because of their character

The following are examples of events that can bother achievement-oriented people:

- Being criticized regarding their performance, whether real or imagined

- Feeling as though they have no control

- Losing their independence

- Feelings of being smothered

- Having difficulty achieving—or failing to reach—a goal

- Being told to do something, not asked

- Not living up to their own expectations

- Giving up control

But what if you're someone who is more in the middle? People who value both interpersonal success *and* achievement can experience difficulty when those two values are in conflict. For example, perhaps someone is invited to attend a friend's wedding, but an opportunity to speak at an important conference presents itself on the same date. Both of these choices provide value—though different kinds of value—and having to choose between them is likely to trigger feelings of distress.

IDENTIFY YOUR VULNERABILITY

• • • • • •

To determine your vulnerability to distress, pay attention to what gets you emotionally activated over the course of the next week. Whenever you're feeling upset, angry, anxious, sad, annoyed, frustrated, down, hurt, fearful, or stressed, make note of the situation that is connected to that emotion. Then ask yourself what specifically bothered you about the situation. Try to identify whether these concerns were related to your desire be socially desirable or to feel a sense of achievement/control (or both). This will allow you to determine what made you vulnerable to distress in that moment. Some examples are provided for you first, followed by spaces for you to fill in your own responses.

EXAMPLE:

Feeling: Nervous

Situation or event: I walked into a party where I only knew the host but no one else.

What bothered you about the situation? I was afraid I would be rejected and that no one would want to talk to me.

Was this related to the desire for social desirability, achievement/control, or both?
Social desirability

Feeling: Annoyed

Situation or event: My partner told me to hurry up when I wanted to take a picture of the scenery on our evening walk.

What bothered you about the situation? I wasn't able to do what I wanted.

Was this related to the desire for social desirability, achievement/control, or both?
Achievement/control

YOUR TURN:

Feeling: _____

Situation or event: _____

What bothered you about the situation?

_____

_____

_____

Was this related to the desire for social desirability, achievement/control, or both?

_____

_____

_____

Feeling: _____

Situation or event: _____

What bothered you about the situation?

_____

_____

_____

Was this related to the desire social desirability, achievement/control, or both?

_____

_____

_____

Feeling: _____

Situation or event: _____

What bothered you about the situation?

_____

_____

_____

Was this related to the desire for social desirability, achievement/control, or both?

_____

_____

_____

LEARNING

We all have different values in life. Getting a sense of what you value is the first step in understanding what activates your self-doubt.

PRACTICE

When you find yourself feeling distressed or upset over the next week, ask yourself whether your concerns are focused on being socially desirable, accomplished, or both.

COPING REMINDER

- Embrace what you value.
- Be careful not to compare yourself to others. Own your own truth.

DOUBT LABELS

We all carry some degree of self-doubt. For some of us, this self-doubt may lie dormant, waiting to rise to the surface when we are under duress or encounter difficulties. For others, this self-doubt is always present, hanging out front and center and negatively impacting the way we interpret and approach situations that come our way.

It's important to point out that not all doubt is bad. When we truly lack the knowledge, experience, or resources to face a situation, doubt can be an ally that protects us from danger or likely negative outcomes. However, when we actually *are* prepared to handle a situation, self-doubt can get in the way and make us feel insecure. It prevents us from reaching our goals and saying yes to opportunities and invitations. It leads us to second-guess every decision we make and every action we take. In turn, we develop doubt labels, which are those nasty names we call ourselves when self-doubt takes control. For example, we may tell ourselves that we're "stupid," "unlovable," or "not good enough."

You may have many doubt labels or just one. Identifying these doubt labels is easier when you know what you value. That's because your values are directly linked to your self-doubt. When you value sociotropy, the doubt labels you use to describe yourself likely reflect themes of social desirability (e.g., "I'm unlovable"), whereas if you value autonomy, they likely reflect themes of competency (e.g., "I'm stupid"). It is also possible to have doubt labels in both domains, especially if you are someone who places value on both interpersonal and achievement-oriented goals.

Regardless of the specific doubt labels that you hold, you don't need to blindly accept the nasty names you tell yourself and allow them to sabotage your path. Pervasive doubt labels are never completely true. Just because you didn't get the job, promotion, or acceptance letter doesn't mean you are a failure. Just because a relationship doesn't work doesn't mean you are undesirable. Just because someone doesn't value your contribution or is disappointed in you doesn't make you bad or unworthy. In order to gain a more accurate view of yourself that promotes self-confidence and goal attainment, it is important to learn how to evaluate the authenticity of your doubt labels. The first step in this process in involves identifying what your doubt labels are to begin with.

EXAMINE YOUR PERCEIVED COMPETENCY AND DESIRABILITY

• • • • • •

To determine the extent to which you hold doubt labels related to themes of competency and social desirability, read through the following statements and indicate whether or not they apply to you.

1.   T or F   Criticism unravels you.

2.   T or F   You are uncomfortable being in control or in charge.

3.   T or F   You struggle with the idea of being independent.

4.   T or F   You don't believe you can achieve your goals.

5.   T or F   You tend to hold yourself to unreasonable expectations.

6.   T or F   You demand perfection.

7.   T or F   Competition scares you.

8.   T or F   You tell yourself that you can't handle the tough stuff.

9.   T or F   Your value as a person is tied to your achievements.

10. T or F   You believe you have to be perfect at everything you do.

11. T or F   You fear rejection.

12. T or F   You feel diminished if you are not included.

13. T or F   You fall apart if someone is upset with you.

14. T or F   You are critical of yourself in social situations.

15. T or F   You don't make yourself a priority.

16. T or F   You jump to negative conclusions when someone doesn't text or call you back.

17. T or F   You need everyone to like you.

18.   T or F   You neglect your own needs in the service of others.

19.   T or F   You think less of yourself when you disappoint others.

20.   T or F   You struggle to voice your own opinion.

 LEARNING

The more items you endorsed as true, the greater your self-doubt. More specifically, items 1–10 reflect a lack of confidence related to perceived competency, whereas items 11–20 reflect a lack of confidence related to perceived social desirability.

....

 PRACTICE

Over the next week, pay attention to the kinds of situations that activate unpleasant emotions, and notice whether they reflect themes of interpersonal success, achievement, or a mixture of both.

....

 COPING REMINDER

- Don't be afraid to recognize what bothers you.
- Just because you are vulnerable doesn't mean you are defeated.

CAPTURE YOUR DOUBT LABELS

· · · · · ·

The following doubt labels share the theme of *social desirability*. Have you ever called yourself any of these names? Check all that apply.

_____ Undesirable   _____ Boring

_____ Unlikeable   _____ Disgusting

_____ Unlovable   _____ Insignificant

_____ Unwanted   _____ Loser

_____ Defective   _____ Plain

_____ Unattractive   _____ Shy

_____ Bad   _____ Ugly

_____ Not good enough to be loved   _____ Unimportant

_____ Worthless   _____ Weird

_____ Uncool   _____ Other: _____

_____ Difficult   _____ Other: _____

_____ Awkward   _____ Other: _____

The following doubt labels share the theme of competency. Have you ever called yourself any of these names? Check all that apply.

_____ Incompetent

_____ Helpless

_____ Failure

_____ Not good enough to succeed

_____ Stupid

_____ Fraud

_____ Inferior

_____ Inadequate

_____ Lazy

_____ Powerless

_____ Weak

_____ Airhead

_____ Don't measure up

_____ Dumb

_____ Incapable

_____ Inept

_____ Useless

_____ Slow

_____ Amateur

_____ Unskilled

_____ Ineffective

_____ Other: _____

_____ Other: _____

_____ Other: _____

LEARNING

Identifying your doubt labels is the first step in building self-confidence. The goal is to not take these labels at face value. Now that you have put a name to your self-doubt, you can start to question its validity.

. . . .

 PRACTICE

Over the next week, pay attention to the times you make a mistake, you have an unpleasant experience, something doesn't go your way, or something bothers you. Notice the labels that you use to describe yourself during these times. Every time you call yourself a nasty name, write it down.

. . . .

 COPING REMINDER

- We all have self-doubt inside of us.

- Do not let your doubt rule the day.

WHERE DOES DOUBT COME FROM?

Self-doubt is shaped by both our biological makeup and our social experiences. Some of us are born sensitive to our environment—for example, we may startle easily, take particular notice of nonverbal cues, be more vulnerable to infections, experience allergic reactions or stomach distress, and experience light sensitivity—while others of us are impervious. These biological characteristics are then shaped by our life experiences. These experiences can involve anything that had a significant impact on us. For example, if you think back to your own childhood, perhaps your family moved around a lot, your parents got divorced, there was substance abuse in the family, or you grew up in a household where multiple generations lived together. You also likely faced certain experiences as a result of your race, age, social status, sexual or gender identity, culture, religion, and so forth. These events all played a role in shaping how you view yourself today.

When it comes to experiences that can elicit self-doubt, many people assume that someone must have been exposed to something traumatic for doubt to arise, such as being subjected to sexual or physical abuse, growing up with a sick parent, or experiencing homelessness, poverty, or abandonment. The assumptions are correct in many cases; these horrific life circumstances can cause self-doubt to run rampant. However, even experiences that are seemingly innocuous can elicit self-doubt, such as being the only "C" student in a family of straight-A siblings, or always being chosen last for the team in gym class.

In addition to life experiences, the messages you hear from other people can influence your self-view. These messages can come from parents, siblings, relatives, neighbors, coaches, teachers, employers, colleagues, coworkers, significant others, friends, childcare providers, peers, strangers, the media, or religious officials. Any message has the potential to negatively affect you—whether it is an overt insult or an insignificant comment that you interpret as an offense. For example, a neighbor might comment, "Your brother is the smart one" or "Your brother is brilliant," and this could lead you to develop the belief that you are not smart.

You might have many significant events or messages that have fueled your self-doubt. But remember, it is not the event or message itself that causes doubt to arise, but how you *interpret* it.

WHERE DOES YOUR DOUBT COME FROM?

• • • • • •

Self-doubt doesn't come out of the blue. It is shaped by your history and how you interpret the events, situations, and experiences in your lives. Some examples of events that can elicit self-doubt include: moving, repeating a grade, parental divorce or separation, legal troubles, health issues, accidents or serious injuries, natural disasters, being fired from a job, unstable housing, family conflict, going through a difficult breakup, or rejection of any kind.

Can you identify the experiences that molded the self-doubt lurking inside of you? These are often tied to specific memories that are embedded in your mind. For example, perhaps in second grade no one wanted to be your partner in class, your seventh-grade teacher was overly critical, or you were picked on as a child. List the events you faced that may have contributed to your negative self-view:

1. _____

2. _____

3. _____

4. _____

Now think of the messages you've heard throughout your life. These could be things you've heard again and again over a period of time, or something said to you just once. Along with the message, include the source—the person who said it to you—and list them out here:

1. Message: _____

   Source: _____

2. Message: _____

   Source: _____

3. Message: _____

   Source: _____

4. Message: _____

   Source: _____

 LEARNING

Your life experiences—whether genuinely traumatic or seemingly insignificant and ordinary—can grow self-doubt and fuel the nasty names you call yourself, as can the messages you hear from others. It is not the event or the message itself, but the meaning you ascribe to it, that fuels self-doubt. However, it is possible your doubt label may not be true! Remind yourself that when you take things too personally, it can make you believe an untruth.

· ·

 PRACTICE

Whenever you notice that you're calling yourself a nasty name, think back to your past and recall those moments that elicited this doubt label.

· ·

 COPING REMINDER

- Because of the things you've gone through, it makes sense that you think about yourself the way you do.

- One situation does not define you.

INEFFECTIVE COMPENSATORY ACTIONS

When self-doubt arises, we often engage in a variety of unhelpful, ineffective actions in an attempt to compensate for our insecurity. Known as ineffective compensatory actions, these behaviors can take one of four forms: avoidance, self-harm, ineffective communication, or perfectionism.

Examples of Ineffective Compensatory Actions	
Avoidance	**Self-Harm**
Quitting	Cutting
Distraction	Suicide
Procrastination	Overexercising
Escape	Substance abuse
Ineffective Communication	**Perfectionism**
Passivity	Overcontrol
Manipulation	People-pleasing
Defensiveness	Worrying
Aggression	Self-criticism

Although these behaviors can alleviate distress in the short term, they cause more problems in the long run. For example, avoidance strategies block us from achieving our goals and addressing what is important. Ineffective communication leads to relational misunderstandings and keeps us from getting our needs met. These strategies all work against us and plant the seeds for self-doubt.

In contrast, strategies that help us achieve our goals include problem-solving, prioritizing tasks, staying focused, being assertive, asking for help, self-soothing in times of stress, and developing realistic standards that build self-confidence. However, even these effective strategies do not work in every situation. The key is the willingness to modify the strategy when it is not working. For example, let's say your team's approach on a committee project is not producing desired results. You could try to use problem-solving techniques or make extra effort to stay focused on the task at hand. If it still does not work out the way you want, then taking complete control of the project might make sense.

Let's spend some time thinking about the behavioral strategies you engage in when self-doubt is activated.

IDENTIFY YOUR INEFFECTIVE COMPENSATORY ACTIONS

· · · · · ·

Put a check mark by any of the behaviors you tend to engage in when you feel self-doubt—even if these behaviors do not produce the results you hope for or even create more problems.

Avoidance:

_____ Quitting

_____ Distracting yourself

_____ Procrastinating on tasks

_____ Escaping social situations

_____ Numbing out

_____ Making excuses

_____ Not answering calls, texts, or emails

Self-Harm:

_____ Cutting

_____ Burning

_____ Overexercising

_____ Using drugs

_____ Drinking to excess

_____ Attempting suicide

_____ Starving yourself

Ineffective Communication:

_____ Not voicing your needs

_____ Manipulating others

_____ Becoming defensive

_____ Lashing out

_____ Exploiting others

_____ Interrupting

_____ Bullying or intimidating others

Perfectionism:

_____ Trying to control everything

_____ People-pleasing

_____ Worrying

_____ Criticizing yourself

_____ Micromanaging

_____ Overworking

_____ Avoiding new activities

Are there any other behaviors that you fall back on when faced with a challenge?

1. _____

2. _____

3. _____

 LEARNING

Although ineffective compensatory actions might help you get what you want in the short term, they come with a steep price and only move you further away from your values. In contrast, effective actions help you face life's challenges and build self-confidence.

 PRACTICE

Over the next week, every time you notice you have engaged in an ineffective compensatory behavior (or have the urge to do so), try replacing it with a more effective action (or see if you can delay the urge to engage in the ineffective behavior).

 COPING REMINDER

- You have the power to choose a course of action that serves your best interest.

- You can resist the urge to pursue an ineffective strategy and choose a more effective one instead.

RULES AND ASSUMPTIONS

Often, the ineffective compensatory actions we engage in are guided by a set of rules and assumptions that we impose on ourselves. Rules are demanding, unrealistic expectations that are typically unattainable or unavoidable. These rules are often characterized by words such as *must*, *ought*, *have to*, *need to*, or *should*. For example: "I have to be perfect at all times" and "Everyone needs to like me." However, since everyone makes mistakes—and since it's impossible to be liked by everyone—these rules only serve to fuel self-doubt.

Rules are closely connected with conditional assumptions, which take the form of "if/then" statements that link your ineffective compensatory actions with your underlying insecurity. That is, conditional assumptions arise in relation to your doubt labels. These assumptions can take either positive or negative forms. Positive assumptions are associated with the belief that you need to behave in certain manner in order to ensure a positive or desirable outcome. For example, someone might assume, "If I keep my opinions to myself, then people will like me." In this case, the belief that they are unlikeable (doubt label) is leading them to be overly passive in their relationships (compensatory behavior). This conditional assumption then reinforces the rule "I need to keep my opinions to myself."

In contrast, negative assumptions are associated with the belief that failing to behave in a certain way will result in a negative or undesirable outcome. They reflect what you fear will happen if you don't hide your self-doubt. For example, someone might assume, "If I am not perfect, then I will fail." Here, the underlying belief that they are incompetent (doubt label) is driving the perfectionism (compensatory behavior). As a result, the person may hold the rule "I must be perfect at all times."

Both positive and negative conditional assumptions (and subsequent compensatory behaviors) only serve to reinforce self-doubt.

IDENTIFY YOUR RULES
AND ASSUMPTIONS

· · · · · ·

Unwritten internal rules and assumptions may unknowingly guide your behavior. Becoming aware of these will help you choose more effective behaviors. First, name some rules that you impose on yourself. These are the unrealistic expectations that you hold yourself to, such as "I must be perfect" or "Everyone has to like me."

Example: I should keep my opinions to myself.

1. _____

2. _____

3. _____

Next, name some assumptions that you believe to be true. These are the "if/then" statements that link your underlying doubt label with your compensatory behaviors. First state the positive conditional assumption, which is *the strategy you use to protect your doubt from being activated*. Next, write out the negative conditional assumption, or *what you fear will happen if you don't behave a certain way*. The "then" portion of your "if/then" statements will likely reveal your underlying doubt label. Some examples are provided for you first, followed by spaces for you to fill in your own responses.

EXAMPLE:

Positive: If I _keep my opinions to myself_, then _people will like me_ .

Negative: If I _voice my opinion_ , then _people won't like me_ .

Doubt label: _I'm unlikeable_

Positive: If I _overexercise_ , then _people will find me attractive_ .

Negative: If I _don't overexercise_ , then _people will find me unattractive_ .

Doubt label: _I'm unattractive_

YOUR TURN:

Positive: If I _____, then _____.

Negative: If I _____, then _____.

Doubt label: _____

Positive: If I _____, then _____.

Negative: If I _____, then _____.

Doubt label: _____

Positive: If I _____, then _____.

Negative: If I _____, then _____.

Doubt label: _____

LEARNING

Rules and assumptions only serve to fuel self-doubt, steal your courage, and block the path to your goals and dreams.

PRACTICE

Capture the rules and assumptions that pop up in your everyday life. See if you can identify the self-doubt that is linked to your rules and assumptions. Try breaking your rule and see what happens.

COPING REMINDER

- The rules you hold yourself to are not set in stone. You have the power to evaluate, modify, revise, and even break them.

- Assumptions are just that—assumptions, not facts. They don't have to rule the day.

3

GOAL-DIRECTED THERAPY

PROBLEM LIST

You are here because you want to feel better and function more effectively in your day-to-day life. In order to make that happen, it's important to take a goal-directed approach as you read this book, meaning that you'll want to set *specific* goals that you want to accomplish. But to do that, you first need to identify the problems, stressors, difficulties, and insecurities you are facing. Gaining a clear understanding of your problems allows you to carve out a clear path to your desired outcome.

To identify your biggest problems, ask yourself why you picked up this book. What is the biggest source of stress or concern in your life? Are you having difficulties with your work performance? Your self-esteem? Your anxiety? Your relationships? Your finances? Perhaps there are many things in life that are bothering you right now. In fact, it is common for problems in one area to lead to problems in another area. For example, if you are struggling with grief, depression, anxiety, or anger, it can lead to substance use, interpersonal conflict, and an inability to function at work, at school, or in the home—which can lead to or exacerbate financial, housing, or legal issues. Let's drill down to understand the core of your problem.

DEFINE YOUR PROBLEMS

• • • • • •

The goal of this worksheet is to identify the specific problems you want to address. Read through the various problem areas to create your personal problem list. Though you should consider each individual prompt, you do not have to respond to each question; instead, focus only on those items that cause problems for you.

Once you create your list, make sure to also describe *how* each area is a problem for you (or why other people think it is a problem for you).

Daily Living

Think about a normal day for you. Do you take care of tasks that need to be completed? Do you make and keep your appointments? Do you get to school or work on time? Do you struggle to get out of bed? Get showered? Get dressed? Leave your home? Are you getting the right amount of sleep for you? Are you eating well enough? Do you make time for activities that you enjoy?

_____

_____

_____

_____

_____

_____

Emotional

Think about your mental health. Are you depressed, anxious, panicked, angry, irritable, frustrated, worried, confused, or manic? Are there other emotions that are impacting your day-to-day life? Do you tend to view the glass as half empty? Do you overthink or obsess over situations? Are you always on edge when others seem relaxed? Do you say no to things when you really want to say yes (or vice versa)? Do you have thoughts of death or suicide?

_____

_____

_____

_____

_____

_____

Interpersonal

Think about how you interact with other people. Are you experiencing conflict in your relationships? Do you find yourself lashing out at others? Do you struggle in social situations? Are you always on the defensive? Do have a difficult time starting a conversation or keeping one going? Do you have trouble communicating? Are you a people pleaser? Do you have trouble saying no? Are you comfortable asserting yourself? Do you often feel left out or ignored?

_____

_____

_____

_____

_____

_____

Self-Esteem

Think about how you view yourself. Do you doubt yourself? Do you worry about your competency? Your intelligence? Do you feel like you're not progressing enough at your job or in your field? Do you feel like you're never good enough? Or that you're an impostor? Do these doubts get in your way, causing you to always second-guess yourself or question your every move?

_____

_____

_____

_____

_____

_____

_____

Medical

Think about how you feel physically. Is stress physically affecting your body? Are you struggling with uncomfortable physical symptoms, such as acid reflux, nausea, diarrhea, muscle tension, headaches, fatigue, dizziness, or a feeling of heaviness in your body? Is stress raising your blood pressure or increasing your heart rate?

_____

_____

_____

_____

_____

_____

_____

School/Work

Think about your school or work life. Are you experiencing difficulties at school or work? Do you struggle with procrastination? Do you have trouble prioritizing and completing your work? Do you have trouble concentrating or staying focused? Does daydreaming interfere with your productivity? Are you falling behind on tasks? Do you get terribly anxious before a test (or a work performance) where you are being evaluated?

_____

_____

_____

_____

_____

_____

Appearance

Think about how you see yourself. Do you like what you see when you look in the mirror? Are you unhappy with your appearance, weight, coordination, or strength? Have you had any recent changes in your weight, mobility, or fitness? Are you critical of how your body is working for you?

_____

_____

_____

_____

_____

_____

Financial

Think about the status of your finances. Are your finances a source of concern? Are you late on paying bills? Do you live within a budget? Have you defaulted on your rent, mortgage, health insurance, or other bills? Do you struggle to make ends meet? Do you worry that you won't be able to financially take care of other family members?

_____

_____

_____

_____

_____

_____

Legal

Think about any legal trouble you've experienced. Have you had any past legal troubles, like being arrested or convicted of a crime? Do you have any pending or unresolved court cases? Do you regularly engage in activities that could get you into trouble with the law?

_____

_____

_____

_____

_____

_____

Housing

Think about your housing situation. Is unstable housing a concern, whether due to living in an overcrowded household, moving frequently, or having to stay with friends or family? Are you experiencing any specific difficulties with the people you live with? Do you feel so overwhelmed with your household responsibilities that it paralyzes you from getting anything done?

_____

_____

_____

_____

_____

_____

Substance Use

Think about any substances you use. Do you drink or use any substances with more frequency or to a greater amount than you would like? Do you use substances to numb yourself out or quiet your brain? Is your substance use resulting in negative consequences, like blackouts, withdrawal symptoms, strained relationships, or legal problems?

_____

_____

_____

_____

_____

_____

Now look through your notes to the previous questions and create a problem list by writing out all your specific difficulties. When writing out your list, make sure you have clearly defined *why* each problem is a problem for you. For example, if you listed "anxiety" as a problem, perhaps it is interfering with your life because it prevents you from making friends, diminishes your self-confidence, and causes you to drink more than you would like. Larger problems will likely cross over several categories. Understanding *how* your problem impacts you will make for a more specific and clear problem list.

1. _____

_____

_____

2. _____

_____

_____

3. _____

_____

_____

4. _____

_____

_____

5. _____

_____

_____

6. _____

_____

_____

LEARNING

Creating a problem list allows you to recognize what it is that you want to work on changing. It is the first step in moving toward your desired outcome. The goal is to make your list as concrete and specific as possible so that you can come up with concrete and specific solutions.

....

 ## PRACTICE

Continue to refine your problem list so you know exactly what you want to work on changing.

....

 ## COPING REMINDER

- Understanding your problems will help you move toward where you want to go.

- Everyone has problems, not just you.

GOAL LIST

Now that you've identified the problems in your life, it is time to set some goals that lead you in the direction of your desired outcome. Although setting a goal sounds easy enough, it is not! Just like you can't expect to jump straight to the top of a ladder from the ground, you can't expect to achieve all your goals at once. Instead, it is important to break down your goals into small, manageable pieces—one rung of the ladder at a time—so you have a clear idea of what you need to do. This also helps you get out of the all-or-nothing mentality so you can give yourself credit for each step that you take in pursuit or your goals. This will help your mood and motivation.

In order to help you break down goals into more manageable components, you'll want to make sure that your goals are concrete, realistic, and something you can measure. Measurable goals allow you to monitor your progress so you can know what's working (and what's not working), which gives you an opportunity to applaud your success or change directions when needed. It is also important to set attainable goals, as unrealistic goals will get in your way and prevent you from moving forward.

For example, let's say that anxiety is one of the problems you identified on the previous worksheet and that your overall goal is to "reduce social anxiety." Although this is absolutely attainable, there is nothing in this statement that will mark your progress as you move forward. In this case, you can narrow down your goal into something more well-defined and measurable by listing out the specific behaviors or steps you'll need to take to reach this goal. For example, you might make goals to start conversations with other coworkers, ask someone to lunch, accept invitations to events, or speak up in meetings. Examples of other goals might be to improve your sleep habits, strengthen a skill or strategy, make more time to engage in leisure activities, change your drinking habits, enhance your physical health, reconnect with friends, save more money, set firmer boundaries in your relationships, improve your self-image, or achieve something new in your personal or professional life.

Keep track of your progress as you take specific steps or show behaviors toward your goal. This can be done however you see fit. For example, you might log your eating habits in a notebook or record days of going to social events on a calendar. It also can be helpful to take account of the times that you do *not* succeed in taking steps forward. For instance, you may be working to set more boundaries with your parents but agree to visit them, even though you are swamped with work, because you said no last time. Just because you did not take a step forward does not necessarily mean you have regressed. Being aware of the factors that have affected one decision may be able to influence your next decision.

Let's spend some time breaking down your broader goals into more actionable and concrete components, as well as ensuring that these goals make sense for you.

GOAL LIST:
HOW YOU CAN MAKE YOUR PROBLEMS LESS OF A PROBLEM?

• • • • • •

Goals represent the solutions to the problems that you have identified in your life. They are a way to make your problems less of a problem. Use this space to create a list of specific, concrete, and measurable goals that you'd like to work on. Two examples are provided for you first, provided by space to create your own goal list.

EXAMPLE:

What is the goal?	I will reduce my alcohol consumption.
What specifically will you do to achieve this goal?	Eliminate alcohol on work nights. Limit myself to no more than two drinks on Friday and Saturday. Try having no drinks at all and try a mocktail instead.
How will you keep track of your progress?	I will keep a log of my alcohol consumption on my phone.

What is the goal?	I will set limits with people and be able to say no.
What specifically will you do to achieve this goal?	Don't automatically say yes. Be willing to say no when it is reasonable to do so. Express myself assertively and ask for what I want.
How will you keep track of your progress?	Every time I say no or set a limit, I'll put a coin in a jar and make sure it continues to fill up.

YOUR TURN:

What is the goal?	
What specifically will you do to achieve this goal?	
How will you keep track of your progress?	

What is the goal?	
What specifically will you do to achieve this goal?	
How will you keep track of your progress?	

What is the goal?	
What specifically will you do to achieve this goal?	
How will you keep track of your progress?	

LEARNING

Goals are concrete, obtainable solutions that make your problems less of a problem.

PRACTICE

Pick one goal from your list, and decide on a specific step you can take this week to help you move toward achieving this goal.

COPING REMINDER

- Having specific goals means you can work on your problems.
- Having a goal is motivation to do the work.

DOES IT MAKE SENSE TO WORK ON MY GOALS?

• • • • • •

Making changes on your own behalf is difficult. Confronting your problems will not come without some complications. You will likely need to go outside your comfort zone. But a clear rationale as to the "why" behind your goals can help you move past these hurdles and propel you toward the finish line. By clearly understanding the advantages and disadvantages of your goal, you can come to realize why your goals make sense—even if there is a downside to doing the work—which can motivate you to make *you* the priority. Think of it as an investment in you. Any investment takes thoughtfulness, attention, time, and action. Use the space below to think through the advantages and disadvantages of doing and not doing the work.

	Advantages	Disadvantages
Doing the work		
Not doing the work		

Once you've listed all the advantages and disadvantages of doing (or not doing) the work, tally up the number of responses in each quadrant. How do the advantages and disadvantages compare? Does it make sense to work toward your goal?

_____

_____

_____

_____

_____

_____

_____

_____

_____

LEARNING

Making change of any kind is hard, even when this change is in pursuit of your goals. By looking at the advantages and disadvantages of working on your goals, you can realize whether it makes sense to do the work, even when there is a downside to doing so.

PRACTICE

Continue working on your goals list, taking one step each day that moves you closer toward this goal. Whenever you feel tempted to avoid taking action, remind yourself why it makes sense to work on this goal to keep moving forward.

COPING REMINDER

- Change is hard, but the end result is worth it.
- The advantages will outweigh the disadvantages, so get to work on your goals.

DOING THE WORK

As with any skill in life, you cannot develop the fundamental skills of wellness without practice. Daily practice—or what is known as "homework" in school—is a way to put everything you've read so far into action so you can make the changes necessary to gain the happiness you desire. This homework is an opportunity to rehearse your skills, apply them in the real world, and reinforce what you've learned. It validates that you are working on yourself, which gives you hope that you can achieve the future you want and keeps you moving forward.

Since practicing skills isn't always easy, it can be tempting to procrastinate, distract yourself from, or delay doing homework. However, it's important to remember that these are all forms of avoidance, which you learned in chapter 1 is a type of ineffective compensatory action. Although avoidance helps you sidestep discomfort in the moment, it leads to bigger problems in the long run because your problems remain unresolved. The only way to overcome a problem is to face it head-on. And doing weekly homework provides you with an opportunity to do just that.

WEEKLY HOMEWORK

• • • • • •

To start making changes and moving yourself toward the life you want, open up your calendar and make a weekly plan to complete homework assignments that are relevant to the goals you are working on. You'll want to pick specific days and times of the week to increase the likelihood that you will follow through on these tasks. Set reminders or alarms if necessary. To keep yourself motivated, remind yourself of the "why" behind this assignment and set a clear objective and plan by describing the "who, what, when, where, and why" for your assignment. An example response is provided for you after each prompt, followed by space for you to fill in your own responses.

Assign yourself weekly homework that is relevant to the goals you are working on.

Example: *I will find two times this week to do something social with friends.*

_____

_____

_____

_____

_____

Why does it makes sense to do this homework?

Example: *I am happier when I am in the company of others, and I am trying to improve my mood.*

_____

_____

_____

_____

_____

Make a clear objective and plan: When, whom, where, what, how long, and how often?

Example: On Tuesday or Wednesday, I'll ask a friend to walk with me after work. On Friday or Saturday, I will ask a friend to join me for dinner.

_____

_____

_____

_____

_____

LEARNING

The only way to achieve your goals is to work on them. Although putting in the work can be hard and even uncomfortable at times, it will help you build the life you want in the long run.

PRACTICE

Pick two specific goals to practice this week, and make an appointment with yourself at a specific time to work on those goals. Don't let excuses or avoidance get in your way. Remind yourself why it makes sense to get to work.

COPING REMINDER

- Homework moves you toward what you want and puts you in control.
- You have to do the work to reap the rewards.

4

DEPRESSION

ARE YOU DEPRESSED?

Although we all experience difficult moments throughout our lives, there is a difference between sadness, grief, and depression. Sadness is a normal human response to the ebbs and flows of life. It is a transient feeling that we experience when confronted with difficulty, stress, or emotional pain. Like sadness, grief is also a universal human experience, but it occurs following a tremendous loss of a loved one. Often, feelings of sadness, fear, anger, and loneliness accompany grief.

While sadness and grief are both universal human experiences, depression is not. Depression is a constant state of sadness in which you lose interest in things that used to bring you joy, which stops you from engaging in normal day-to-day activities. Sometimes grief can evolve into depression when it persists long after the loss has occurred, which can lead people to struggle to move on with their life. They may believe, "I can never be happy again" or "I cannot survive alone."

When you are depressed, regardless of its cause, your thinking becomes negatively biased. You start to see every aspect of your life through a distorted lens, leading you to see yourself, your relationships, and the future in the most pessimistic way. In turn, you may engage in a variety of self-defeating behaviors like isolation, withdrawal, avoidance, substance use, and sometimes even suicidality, which only serves to perpetuate the depression.

PATIENT HEALTH QUESTIONNAIRE (PHQ-9)*

• • • • • •

If you have been feeling down or blue lately, this tool can help you evaluate if you may be experiencing depression. However, it is not intended to take the place of a professional diagnosis.

Over the last two weeks, how often have you been bothered by any of the following problems?

Not at all	Several days	More than half the days	Nearly every day
0	1	2	3

_____ 1. Little interest or pleasure in doing things

_____ 2. Feeling down, depressed, or hopeless

_____ 3. Trouble falling or staying asleep or sleeping too much

_____ 4. Feeling tired or having little energy

_____ 5. Poor appetite or overeating

_____ 6. Feeling bad about yourself—or that you are a failure or have let yourself or your family down

_____ 7. Trouble concentrating on things, such as reading the newspaper or watching TV

_____ 8. Moving or thinking so slowly that other people could have noticed (or the opposite—being so fidgety or restless that you have been moving around more than usual)

_____ 9. Thoughts that you would be better off dead or of hurting yourself in some way

_____ **Total score**

* Developed by Drs. Robert L. Spitzer, Janet B.W. Williams, Kurt Kroenke and colleagues, with an educational grant from Pfizer Inc. No permission required to reproduce, translate, display, or distribute.

If you checked off *any* problem on this questionnaire, how *difficult* have these problems made it for you to do your work, take care of things at home, or get along with other people?

☐ Not difficult at all   ☐ Somewhat difficult   ☐ Very difficult   ☐ Extremely difficult

LEARNING

This inventory helped you take your depression temperature. You can interpret your scores with the following guidelines:

Minimal depression	0–4
Mild depression	5–9
Moderate depression	10–14
Moderately severe depression	15–19
Severe depression	20–27

It is important to know that depression can impact you whether your symptoms are minimal or severe. When you are depressed, everything seems negative, nothing feels good, and it becomes hard to function.

PRACTICE

Every two weeks, do a mental health check-in by measuring your depression symptoms again, and see whether the principles you are putting into practice are working.

COPING REMINDER

- Depression biases your thinking, so consider that what you are thinking may actually be wrong, exaggerated, or distorted.

- Depression is a problem that doesn't have to define you.

BEHAVIORAL ACTIVATION

Depression steals your energy and makes it harder to do anything. It often feels as though you're walking through mud. The irony of depression is that you must take action in order to battle depression, yet depression convinces you that you cannot act. We so often hear people say, "I will do _____ when the depression lifts, when I feel better, when I have more energy, when I am not so tired, or when I feel like it." However, these thoughts only perpetuate the depression because they block you from taking any sort of action. The truth is, *action precedes motivation.* You can do things even if you are depressed, don't feel well, are tired, or don't feel motivated. Reflecting back on today, there are probably numerous things you've already done that you didn't feel like doing, such getting out bed, taking a shower, getting dressed, making yourself food, cleaning up, running an errand, or going to work.

However, depression biases your perspective and makes you think you are doing less than you are actually doing. This happens, in part, because you compare yourself to everyone else in the world who is not depressed (or to yourself when you were functioning at your best), which diminishes your own accomplishments. Instead of taking credit for the Herculean effort it took to get out of bed or do the dishes, you discount your effort. You also confuse effort with outcome when judging your success. But it is the process—not the outcome—that matters most. For example, if you reach out to a few friends and invite them for lunch (after having avoided people for months), you should view this as an accomplishment, regardless of whether your friends are available to accept the invitation. It is the trying—the effort—that matters.

When considering the actions you can take that can have an impact on your mood, it is important to determine the level of mastery, pleasure, and social interaction associated with each activity. These three areas provide the foundation for well-being. Mastery involves doing things that give you a sense of achievement and that challenge you to grow. Pleasure involves doing things that bring you intrinsic joy. Although joy can arise from tasks that give you a sense of accomplishment, pleasure is more about doing something for the sake of the activity itself. Finally, activities that involve social interaction can take place in person or virtually. It can involve doing something with others in an intimate, friendly, informative, or professional forum—or simply being surrounded by others in a class, a store, or in transit. It is being in the presence of other human beings that counts.

ACTIVITY LOG

• • • • • •

Over the next week, record what you are doing at each hour of the day and what your mood is at that time. It may help at first to set a timer to remind you when it is time to check in again. Use the following scale to describe your mood:

Poor		Below Average		Average		Good		Excellent	
0	1	2	3	4	5	6	7	8	9	10

In addition, make sure to note if each activity fulfills a sense of mastery (M), pleasure (P), or social interaction (S). Keeping this daily log will provide you with objective data about your day—letting you know what you are doing, the impact it has on your mood, and if you are doing activities associated with the three foundations of well-being.

	Monday	Tuesday	Wednesday	Thursday	Friday	Saturday	Sunday
6–7 a.m.							
7–8 a.m.							
8–9 a.m.							
9–10 a.m.							
10–11 a.m.							
11–12 p.m.							

	Monday	Tuesday	Wednesday	Thursday	Friday	Saturday	Sunday
12–1 p.m.							
1–2 p.m.							
2–3 p.m.							
3–4 p.m.							
4–5 p.m.							
5–6 p.m.							
6–7 p.m.							
7–8 p.m.							
8–9 p.m.							
9–10 p.m.							
10–11 p.m.							
11–12 a.m.							
12–6 a.m.							

LEARNING

Self-monitoring can facilitate more action. It makes you aware of how much you are doing and, more importantly, if you are doing activities that enhance (or worsen) your well-being.

PRACTICE

Continue updating your activity log, paying particular attention to what you do and how it makes you feel. If you notice that certain activities seem to elevate your mood, try intentionally scheduling more of these activities into your day. To the extent possible, make sure you are also experiencing a sense of mastery, pleasure, and social connection each day.

COPING REMINDER

- Action precedes motivation.
- You can do things even when you don't feel like it.
- Even seemingly small efforts to take action deserve credit.

HEALTHY HABITS

Nutrition, sleep, and exercise are essential components to wellness—and when they go awry, it can make everything worse. Therefore, as part of behavioral activation, it is crucial to make time in your schedule to fuel your body with nutrient-dense food, get sufficient sleep, and engage in a regular exercise routine. Although it may seem simple, building these healthy habits can not only serve as protective buffer against depression, but it can also help you unravel its hold.

Nutrition

When it comes to nutrition and depression, calorie-dense foods that are high in fat and sugar can contribute to lethargy, brain fog, and a worsening of mood. In addition, what, when, and how you eat can impact how you feel. When you forget to eat, ignore your body's needs, or eat to satisfy a psychological need (e.g., eating when you're bored, sad, or lonely), it can affect both your physical and mental energy. By keeping a food diary, you can start to see how the timing of your meals, the quantity of the food you consume, and the type of food you eat all impact your mood. As you begin to see a relationship between these variables, you can make adjustments to your diet and be more intentional about purchasing food options and scheduling mealtimes that promote your well-being. While maintaining a healthy diet won't cure depression, it will help ease your symptoms and boost your mood.

FOOD AND MOOD DIARY

• • • • • •

Over the next week, keep a record of when you eat, what you eat, how much you eat, and your mood before and after each snack or meal. Use the following rating scale to describe your mood:

Poor		Below Average			Average			Good		Excellent
0	1	2	3	4	5	6	7	8	9	10

Time	Food	Amount Eaten	Mood Before	Mood After

Time	Food	Amount Eaten	Mood Before	Mood After

After a week of tracking your food and mood, do you notice any patterns? Are there certain foods that negatively impact your mood or make you feel sluggish? What about foods that boost your mood and energize you?

LEARNING

Healthy eating habits can contribute to your emotional and physical well-being. By monitoring your daily food intake, you can better see the link between food and mood.

PRACTICE

Notice the connection between what you eat, when you eat, and how you feel. If you find that any foods consistently lower your mood, try making changes to this area to see if it pays off. Run different experiments and see which foods work best for you overall.

COPING REMINDER

- Food is fuel for your body, and your body functions best with high-grade fuel.
- What and when you eat matters. Listen to your body and fuel positivity.

Sleep

Equally as important as maintaining a balanced diet is maintaining a healthy sleep schedule. Too little sleep can wreak havoc on your mood, brain, and energy level. It can interfere with your ability to think clearly and concentrate, causing you to experience difficulty retaining information, to become more forgetful, and to make more mistakes. True sleep deprivation can even make you hear or see things that are not actually there. A good test to determine if you are sleep deprived is to close your eyes during the day, and if you fall asleep within 15 minutes, then you are not getting enough sleep. Every person needs a different amount of sleep, but on average, seven to eight hours a night is enough.

If you are experiencing sleep difficulties, such as difficulty falling asleep, frequent nighttime awakenings, or waking earlier than planned, then some basic sleep hygiene tools can help get your sleep back on track. Sleep hygiene simply refers to healthy habits that promote your ability to get a restful night's sleep. These include:

- Learn to associate your bed with sleeping by using your bed only for sleep and sex. Don't watch TV, read, check your phone, or surf the internet in bed. Make sure to also turn off electronic devices one hour before going to sleep.

- Get regular exercise during the day and avoid exercising late into the evening.

- Limit your caffeine and alcohol intake, especially in the afternoon and evening. Try to also avoid eating late at night so your stomach isn't still digesting food when it's time for bed.

- Create a nightly wind-down routine. Our bodies sometimes need a cue to turn off. Try some guided meditation, soothing music, self-massage, or progressive muscle relaxation before bed to let your body know it's time for sleep.

- Go to bed only when you're tired. If you're still awake after 20 minutes, get up and do something relaxing until you feel tired, then try going to bed again. Be careful not to doze off on the couch. Prematurely falling asleep before you have gotten into bed will make it harder to sleep that night. Instead use your fatigue as a cue to immediately head to bed.

- Enhance your sleep environment by keeping the room cool (approximately 65 degrees Fahrenheit), dark (consider room-darkening curtains or an eye mask), and quiet (try earplugs, a fan, or a white noise machine).

- Keep consistent sleep and wake times, even on the weekends. Even if you've had a bad night of sleep, resist the temptation to sleep in the next day. It will make it harder to sleep the following night. Similarly, keep naps to a minimum. When napping is absolutely necessary, limit it to a 20-minute power nap so the architecture of your sleep is not impacted.

In addition, know that even if you have one lousy night of sleep, you can still have a good next day. You can still function effectively after one night of insomnia, so don't be afraid when you have minor sleep difficulties here or there. The key is not to let your fears of not sleeping get in the way of actually sleeping. Instead of worrying about your sleep—for example, "I will mess up at work if I don't have a good night's sleep" or "I will never sleep again"— try replacing these thoughts with more accurate and helpful ones, like "I can do my job even if I am tired" or "I will sleep again even if it's not tonight."

EVALUATE YOUR SLEEP HYGIENE

• • • • • •

To determine what your sleep hygiene looks like, look through the following statements and circle the statement in the column that most applies to you.

Do you…?

1. Use the bed for sleep and sex only	or	Use the bed for watching television, browsing your computer or phone, or doing work
2. Get regular exercise during the day	or	Exercise late in the evening or avoid exercise altogether
3. Cut down on caffeine or limit it to early afternoon	or	Drink excessive caffeine or drink it past 2 or 3 p.m.
4. Avoid drinking alcohol	or	Drink a lot of alcohol
5. Avoid eating or drinking close to bedtime	or	Drink or eat late at night
6. Eat enough to be satisfied	or	Go to bed hungry or eat right before bed
7. Resist the temptation to nap after a bad night of sleep	or	Take long naps to compensate for lack of nighttime sleep
8. Keep a regular sleep schedule, even on the weekends	or	Let yourself sleep in on the weekends
9. Resist the urge to fall asleep on the couch and head up to bed instead	or	Let yourself fall asleep on the couch
10. Sleep in a dark, cool, and quiet room	or	Sleep with a nightlight, in a room that's too warm, or in a noisy environment
11. Turn off electronics one hour before bed	or	Stay up late scrolling on your phone or watching TV

All the items on the left side represent good sleep hygiene, while the items on the right are practices that interfere with sleep. Which column did you circle more items in? If you found that you circled more items in the right side, then your current sleep habits may be interfering with your ability to function at your best. The good news is you can change these habits and get your sleep schedule back on track by simply doing more of the behaviors in the left column.

 LEARNING

Improving your sleep hygiene can fortify you against depression. Making these seemingly small behavioral changes can have a big effect on your sleep (and, in turn, your mood).

 PRACTICE

Follow the guidelines for good sleep hygiene by practicing the actions in the right-hand column. If you find yourself ruminating at night, trying writing down all your worries in a notepad and remind yourself that you'll deal with them tomorrow. Don't lie awake in bed.

 COPING REMINDER

- You have the tools to change your sleep habits.
- Missing one night of sleep or getting one night of bad sleep is not the end of the world.

Exercise

In addition to maintaining healthy eating habits and getting enough sleep, exercising on a regular basis can make a big difference in your mood. That's because when you engage in physical activity, your body releases chemicals known as endorphins, which have a natural mood-boosting effect. To achieve these benefits, it is typically recommended that you engage in some form of aerobic exercise for at least 30 minutes a day, five days a week. Aerobic exercise simply means that it elevates your heart rate, but that doesn't mean you need to put forth high-intensity effort to achieve this effect. Try going on a brisk walk, turning on some music and dancing, taking an online workout class, or even playing an interactive video game. If you need an accountability partner, find someone to work out with and head to the gym or park together.

EXERCISE AND MOOD DIARY

• • • • • •

Over the next week, schedule specific times for exercise, making note of what aerobic activity you did, how long you exercised for, and your mood before and after each activity. Use the following rating scale to describe your mood:

Poor		Below Average			Average		Good			Excellent
0	1	2	3	4	5	6	7	8	9	10

	Activity	Start Time	End Time	Mood Before	Mood After
Monday					
Tuesday					
Wednesday					
Thursday					

	Activity	Start Time	End Time	Mood Before	Mood After
Friday					
Saturday					
Sunday					

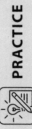

LEARNING

Regular exercise, especially aerobic exercise, promotes a positive mood. Scheduling exercise into your weekly routine helps ensure it will happen.

PRACTICE

Consider putting some form of exercise into your daily routine by figuring out simple opportunities to be more active, whether it's using the stairs, parking farther away, standing more often, or going for short walks throughout the day.

COPING REMINDER

- Exercise is a natural mood booster that fortifies your body and mind.
- Take care of yourself by making exercise happen.

EVALUATE AND UPDATE YOUR SCHEDULE

Now that you've gotten an idea of what your day-to-day schedule is like, including how your eating, sleeping, and exercise habits are tied to your mood, it's time to start gradually incorporating more activities into your routine. The key is to make sure that you put a specific plan in place—and that you include this plan on your activity log. For example, imagine that you run into a friend you haven't seen in a while and you say, "It's so great to see you, let's do dinner sometime." Do you think that doing dinner "sometime" means you are getting together any time soon or even at all? Probably not. Now instead imagine that you ask your friend, "Are you free this Friday or Saturday? There's a great new place I've been wanting to try." In this case, the dinner date is more likely to happen because there is a set plan in place. That's why scheduling your activities is so important: It maximizes the likelihood that you'll get those things done.

As you begin adding planned activities to your activity log, make sure to record whether or not you followed through with the plan, as well as how this impacted your mood. Although it is inevitable that some plans will get canceled from time to time due to factors outside of your control, if you find that you are frequently making excuses and avoiding plans altogether, it's important to look out for any "give-up" thoughts that might be getting in the way. Give-up thoughts are roadblocks that try to convince you to avoid the plan. These thoughts often sound like "I don't feel like it," "It's too hard," "I'll do it later," "I can't do this," or "This won't help."

Whenever you notice these give-up thoughts pop into your head, it's important to replace them with "go-to" thoughts that promote action, like:

- "I don't have to feel like it to take action."

- "I can do things I don't want to do."

- "If I put it off, it will never happen. I need to do it now."

- "It may not be as hard as I think. I can give it a try."

- "I won't know whether or not this will help unless I try."

When you take action, regardless of how much you do or what the end result is, it builds momentum and a sense of accomplishment.

ACTION PLAN

• • • • • •

If you find that give-up thoughts are interfering with your ability to follow through on your activity schedule, use this action plan to deal with these thoughts as they arise. By replacing give-up thoughts with go-to thoughts, you can get unstuck and start moving in the direction of your goals once again.

What are some activities that you have been avoiding?

1. _____

_____

2. _____

_____

3. _____

_____

What are some give-up thoughts that have gotten in the way of being able to do these activities?

1. _____

_____

2. _____

_____

3. _____

_____

To help you get unstuck and move in the direction of action, brainstorm some go-to thoughts that you could use to replace your give-up thoughts.

Give-Up Thought   **Go-To Thought**

1. _____ ➡ 1. _____

   _____   _____

2. _____ ➡ 2. _____

   _____   _____

3. _____ ➡ 3. _____

   _____   _____

Now put your plan into place! The next time you feel tempted to cancel a scheduled activity, repeat these go-to thoughts to yourself so you can take action and stick with your plan. Remember, that taking action doesn't involve making demands of yourself. When you tell yourself that you *have to, must, or should* do something, it won't help. Instead, think of the reasons why it makes sense to take this action. Remind yourself of the reward waiting for you at the end of the activity: You'll feel better, experience pleasure, and grow more confident.

 LEARNING

Putting a plan in place makes it more likely that you will follow through on tasks. Whenever give-up thoughts try to interfere with this plan, remember that action precedes motivation. You don't have to feel a certain way to take action.

. . . .

 PRACTICE

Monitor your activity log, and whenever you notice that you are giving up or avoiding action, use this action plan to turn your give-up thoughts into go-to thoughts.

. . . .

 COPING REMINDER

- Scheduling makes things happen.
- Doing it later means doing it never.
- Doing anything is better than doing nothing.

COGNITIVE RESTRUCTURING

As you've learned, depression clouds your thinking, causing you to see yourself, the world, and the future in a negative light. It's like wearing a pair of glasses with filthy lenses. You can't see the world in an accurate way because of it. Your job is to clean off those glasses so you can see everything without the discoloration of depression. This is the work of cognitive restructuring, in which you work to identify and reframe distorted thoughts into more positive and realistic beliefs. The tools you learned in the behavioral activation section laid the foundation for this cognitive restructuring work, in which you began replacing give-up thoughts with go-to thoughts. Now it's time to dig even deeper so you can address the negative thoughts that are contributing to your depression.

Catch Automatic Thoughts

If you think back to the cognitive model from chapter 1, you'll recall that situations in and of themselves don't cause distress. Rather, it is how you interpret those situations that drives distress. These interpretations arise almost instinctively, without any conscious thought, which is why they are called automatic thoughts. Because these thoughts come to you so automatically, you often don't even notice them and when you do, you blindly accept them as true, even when they're not. Therefore, the first step of cognitive restructuring is to identify these automatic thoughts so you can learn to question their validity or utility.

One way to identify your automatic thoughts is to pay attention to what is going through your mind when you notice a shift in your mood (e.g., suddenly feeling sad, anxious, angry, or irritable) or in your body (e.g., muscle tension, shortness of breath, increased heart rate, tightening your jaw or fists, heaviness, or fatigue). In those moments, ask yourself, "What is going through my mind?" When asking this question, try not to focus on the situation in its entirety (e.g., an argument with your partner), but on *specific* moments where you noticed yourself having a strong physical or emotional reaction (e.g., when your partner insulted you in the midst of that argument). You can have dozens of automatic thoughts, so focusing in on those key moments can help you uncover the specific thoughts associated with your distress.

CATCH YOUR AUTOMATIC THOUGHTS

· · · · · ·

An automatic thought is your interpretation of a specific event or situation. You can even have automatic thoughts about your thoughts. These thoughts can be fleeting phrases or images that pop into your mind. They tend to pack a punch, so it is important to catch them as they arise. Here are some strategies to catch your automatic thoughts:

1 When a strong emotion overtakes you, ask yourself, "What am I thinking right now?" or "What thoughts are connected to that emotion?"

2 When you notice yourself experiencing a strong body sensation, ask yourself "What am I thinking right now?" or "What thoughts are connected to that body sensation?"

3 When you notice yourself acting in a problematic way, ask yourself, "What am I thinking right now?" or "What thoughts are connected to that behavior?"

4 Imagine that a distressing situation is happening to you right now, or think back to a recently distressing time and try to relive it. As you imagine yourself confronting the most emotionally charged aspect of this situation, ask yourself what you are thinking.

5 Ask a friend what they might have thought in response to a particular situation. Notice if your thoughts are similar or different to theirs.

LEARNING

Automatic thoughts arise so quickly that you often don't even realize when they're affecting your mood, body, and behavior. By taking the time to stop and ask yourself, "What am I thinking right now?" you can learn how to capture these thoughts in real time.

 PRACTICE

This week, when you are having a bad day, a stressful day, or a frustrating day, try to reflect on a specific moment that day when you felt a strong emotion or body sensation, and capture what you were thinking at the time.

 COPING REMINDER

- Catching your thoughts sets you up to feel better.
- Use your feelings as a signal to capture your thoughts.

COLLECT MORE AUTOMATIC THOUGHTS, ASSUMPTIONS, AND DOUBT LABELS

When you're faced with a stressful or upsetting situation, you can experience multiple automatic thoughts about that situation. Oftentimes, the first automatic thought that you're able to capture only represents the tip of the iceberg, so it is important to go deeper and look for the conditional assumptions and doubt labels that are driving this thought. For example, let's say that your boss calls you in for a meeting and the first thought that comes to mind is "I'm going to get fired." In this case, your automatic thought is likely being driven by the assumption "If my boss wants to meet with me, then it must be about something bad," and accompanying doubt label might be "I'm a fraud."

Remember that conditional assumptions are "if/then" rules that guide your behavior, regardless of their truth or helpfulness. Behind each conditional assumption is a doubt label that you hold about yourself. This self-doubt is the underlying culprit that leads you to view situations through a distorted lens. When your self-doubt is in charge, you experience more intense emotions and your behaviors become more extreme. Therefore, it is crucial to uncover these underlying assumptions and doubt labels in order to determine what is driving your automatic thoughts. To do so, you can ask yourself a series of probing questions, such as:

- What about this bothers you?

- What are you worried that might mean?

- And what about this is a problem for you?

- And if it is true, what that would that mean?

- What does this say about you?

- What is the worst thing about this?

Be sure to note that the answers to these questions are not necessarily true. However, they will help you capture the additional automatic thoughts, assumptions, and doubt labels driving your distress. For example, let's say you don't get invited to your coworker's party. In this case, you can use the probing questions to uncover specifically what about that event or situation upset you, including what underlying self-doubt it might be connected to:

- What about this bothers you? I'm the only person I know who wasn't invited.
  (automatic thought)

- What does this say about you? That my coworkers don't like me. If they liked me, then they would have invited me.
  (conditional assumption)

- What does this mean about you? I am unlikeable.
  (doubt label)

COLLECT YOUR THOUGHTS, ASSUMPTIONS, AND DOUBT LABELS

• • • • • •

Use this exercise to uncover the underlying conditional assumptions and doubt labels that are driving your negative automatic thoughts. If you are having trouble identifying the underlying meaning behind your thoughts, remember to ask yourself the previous probing questions to find out what is really going on. Some examples are provided for you first, followed by spaces for you to fill in your own responses.

EXAMPLE:

Situation: Nick has been working long hours at his new job and was told the team would be done by 7 p.m. that night. His manager contacted him shortly before 7 p.m. and piled on more work, requiring everyone to stay well beyond the promised finish time.

Automatic thought: I shouldn't have to stay, nothing I do is ever enough.

Assumption: If I had done a more thorough job, then we wouldn't have to stay.

Doubt belief: I am inadequate.

Situation: Suzi texted several of her friends about making plans for Friday night, but no one responded.

Automatic thought: I'm not part of the group. Nobody wants to make plans with me.

Assumption: If people don't text me back, then they don't want to be with me.

Doubt belief: I am unlikeable.

YOUR TURN:

Think about a recently upsetting situation. What was the specific situation?

_____

_____

What automatic thoughts came up for you?

_____

_____

What conditional assumptions did you have?

_____

_____

What is your possible doubt label?

_____

_____

Think about a recently upsetting situation. What was the specific situation?

_____

_____

What automatic thoughts came up for you?

_____

_____

What conditional assumptions did you have?

_____

_____

What is your possible doubt label?

_____

_____

LEARNING

Automatic thoughts only represent what is going on at the surface. Underneath there are conditional assumptions and doubt labels driving these thoughts. And when doubt guides your thoughts, it is more likely to result in an incorrect interpretation of the situation.

 PRACTICE

Over the next week, pay attention when you experience an upsetting situation. Identify the automatic thoughts driving your distress and then go even further by uncovering the associated conditional assumptions and doubt label. Take note if you continue to have the same assumptions and if your conclusion about yourself involves a reoccurring negative theme.

 COPING REMINDER

- Faulty beliefs can lead to invalid thoughts and assumptions.
- Doubt doesn't have to color your day.

THINKING ERRORS

When working to understand the automatic thoughts that are driving your distress, it is helpful to identify common thinking errors that might be getting in the way. Unlike automatic thoughts, that are tied to specific situations, thinking errors are broader patterns of irrational thinking that may characterize many of those automatic thoughts. When your perceptions are biased, distorted, or exaggerated, thinking errors are often the culprit. Identifying those thinking errors can help you recognize that you may not be seeing the truth, or the whole truth, of a situation. The following are some common thinking errors that people often make.

Extreme thinking involves seeing everything in all-or-nothing terms, with no shades of gray in between. This way of thinking says that things are either good or bad, a success or failure, perfect or a disaster. The problem with extreme thinking is that it prevents you from seeing the nuances of life. Things are rarely "all good" or "all bad"— more often than not, they fall somewhere in between. You can correct extreme thinking by looking at the bigger picture and taking into account the positives and negatives of each situation. This allows you to draw more accurate conclusions. For example, instead of thinking, "The party was a complete disaster," you might think, "Overall the party was great and everyone had a good time, but the desserts were awful."

Depending on your emotions involves using your emotions as a guide rather than looking at the facts. With this thinking error, you treat your emotions as truths. For example, you might say, "I feel like I made a bad impression, so I must have messed up" or "I feel incompetent, so I must be worthless." Although emotions are an important source of information, they can lead to unreliable and subjective conclusions when you don't consider the objective facts. It is important to look beyond your feelings and ask yourself if the facts of the situation match up. If your feelings and the facts are at odds, consider letting the facts win. For example, instead of thinking, "I feel like I made a bad impression," you could look at the facts and say, "They said they really enjoyed my company and invited me to join them next weekend."

Negative self-labeling involves using nasty names to describe yourself. The problem with negative self-labeling is that you're making assumptions about your character on the basis of one bad experience. For example, you might call yourself "stupid" after you make one mistake, or you might call yourself a "loser" when your friend tells you that she's too busy to hang out this weekend. However, the reality is that no one event, experience, or outcome can define us, even if it seems like a very big or very important one. We are all a composite of many skills, abilities, strengths, personality characteristics, and physical features. To overcome this thinking error, it is important to recognize that one mistake or shortcoming doesn't define who you are.

Zooming in on the negative involves taking a magnifying glass to everything negative in your life while ignoring, minimizing, or discrediting anything positive or neutral that occurs. When you zoom in on the negative, you only focus on the worst part of any situation. For example, you might receive a less-than-perfect review on your performance evaluation and take this to mean that you are doing a poor job. To gain a more balanced perspective, you need to step back and look at the whole situation. For example, while your performance review might not have been perfect, your boss might have given you ample praise for your work ethic and still view you as a top employee.

Discounting the positives is another type of thinking error that often goes hand in hand with zooming in on the negative. When you discount the positive, you never give yourself credit for anything that you accomplish in life. Instead of acknowledging that your talents, efforts, or skills contributed to a positive outcome, you write it off as sheer luck or tell yourself that it doesn't count. For example, if you receive an A on an exam, you might tell yourself that it was an easy test and that your grade has nothing to do with your intelligence or the fact that you studied hard to learn the material. You can stop discounting the positives by acknowledging your victories rather than attributing them to luck or some other external factor.

Catastrophizing involves turning a snowball into an avalanche. You imagine that the worst-case scenario is likely to occur (even when there is evidence to the contrary), or you underestimate your ability to cope if this feared outcome were to happen. For example, if your teenager misses their agreed-upon curfew, you assume that they've gotten into some terrible car accident. Or if you get a voice mail from your boss on a Friday night, you think it must be because you're getting fired. You can address catastrophizing by consider all possible outcomes, including the worst, best, and most likely scenarios.

Fortune telling involves making negative predictions about the future and always assuming that things will turn out badly—even when you have little evidence to support those predictions. For example, someone who experiences a painful breakup with her partner may think, "I will never find love again" without even trying to put herself out there. The reality is that we cannot accurately predict the future, so assuming the worst only causes undo suffering. It also prevents you from working toward your goals.

Mind reading happens when you jump to conclusions about what people are thinking about you, which can lead you to become your own worst critic and naysayer. For example, if you ask a friend over to help you install your new thermostat, you may tell yourself, "He thinks I'm such a moron." However, just as you cannot predict the future, you cannot read someone else's mind. Instead, you can examine the evidence or assertively ask what the other person is thinking. In the case of the thermostat, it is quite possible that your friend is thinking, "These things are such a pain in the neck to install. I wish someone had been there to help me."

Personalizing involves taking things personally when they actually have nothing to do with you at all. For example, if a store clerk is short with you, you automatically jump to the conclusion that they don't like you. When you take responsibility for others' negative behavior, you assume inappropriate blame and feel bad about yourself. To address this thinking error, it is important to consider that people are often unaware of their behavior, let alone the impact it is having on others. Instead, consider more plausible explanations for the other person's actions. For example, it is possible the store clerk was short with you because they were having a bad day or are unhappy at their job.

Should and must statements are subjective rules that you impose on yourself and others with words like *should* or *must*. They dictate how you believe things should play out in the world. For example, you might tell yourself that everyone should be on time, that your friend should have called you back, or that you must get every task done today. However, when you place such demanding expectations on yourself or others, it just guarantees frustration because the world doesn't always operate the way you want it to. Instead, it is important to accept that you are powerless to control how others think, feel, or behave. In addition, you can replace should or must statements with a preference statement or a request instead, which can lessen your distress. For example, instead of thinking, "I must get everything done today," you might think, "I would be nice to get everything done today, but I might not be able to."

When you recall specific thoughts you have had, you may find that many of them fit the description of thinking errors from the previous list. These general ways of thinking often show up in your automatic thoughts. The goal is to identify your common thinking errors so you can start replacing them with less biased and distorted thoughts.

THINKING ERRORS

· · · · · ·

To get into the habit of identifying thinking errors, read through the following scenarios and describe the thinking error that characterizes each situation. There may be multiple thinking errors for each statement. An answer key is provided at the end of the worksheet.

1. When Ramon considers trying out for the soccer team, he thinks, "I just don't have what it takes to make it."

   Thinking errors: _____

   _____

   _____

2. Two people RSVP *no* to Berna's event and she thinks, "No one will be there."

   Thinking errors: _____

   _____

   _____

3. A work project is stressing Chris out and he thinks, "I'm sure it won't turn out well."

   Thinking errors: _____

   _____

   _____

4. Domingo's partner has a tense tone of voice on the phone, leading him to think, "She must be mad at me."

   Thinking errors: _____

   _____

   _____

5. Mercedes didn't get the job she applied for and thinks to herself, "I'll never get a job."

Thinking errors: _____

_____

_____

6. Annabel received her performance review, and it was overall very positive, except the issue of her tardiness. She tells herself, "This is a terrible review."

Thinking errors: _____

_____

_____

7. Lamar has been asked to give a toast and thinks, "I am going to make a fool of myself."

Thinking errors: _____

_____

_____

8. When Shelly's partner declines a second date with her, she thinks, "I am such a loser."

Thinking errors: _____

_____

_____

9. Andre has a back injury, but when his friend asks him to help her move, he thinks, "I should help because she is a good friend."

Thinking errors: _____

_____

_____

10. After Lucille receives a compliment from her coworker and boss, she tells herself, "They don't mean it, they are just being nice."

Thinking errors: _____

_____

_____

 LEARNING

Thinking errors are filters that cause you to view the world in a biased or distorted way. By building an awareness of what thinking errors look like, you'll be better able to notice when you make these errors in your life. Once you recognize the errors, you can more quickly realize when your automatic thoughts are not true.

 PRACTICE

Over the next week, pay attention to each time you use one of these thinking errors throughout the day. Notice which ones you tend to use the most and keep a running list.

 COPING REMINDER

- Thinking errors are called errors for a reason. They do not reflect reality.

- By turning off the filters, you can see the world in a more accurate way.

Answer Key: (1) Fortune telling, Depending on your emotions. (2) Extreme thinking, Catastrophizing. (3) Depending on your emotions, Fortune telling. (4) Personalizing, Mind reading. (5) Catastrophizing, Extreme thinking. (6) Zooming in on the negative, Extreme thinking. (7) Labeling, Fortune telling. (8) Labeling, Mind reading. (9). Should and must statements. (10) Discounting the positives.

EVALUATE YOUR AUTOMATIC THOUGHTS

Although it is common to blindly accept your automatic thoughts at face value, they are not always true. Automatic thoughts can be completely false or distorted, or they may be true or at least reflect a kernel of truth. Therefore, it is important to examine the validity of your thoughts so you can correct and modify any inaccurate conclusions you've made about yourself. In doing so, you can stop attaching meaning to unhelpful or untrue thoughts that are contributing to unnecessary distress in your life.

To correct inaccurate thinking, you'll need to dissect any partially true thoughts, separate truth from exaggeration, engage in problem-solving when faced with unhelpful but realistic thoughts, and modify unhelpful thoughts into more helpful ones. Given that not every negative thought you have is completely wrong, the goal is not to indiscriminately replace negative thoughts with positive thoughts. Rather, it is to replace inaccurate and unhelpful thoughts with more accurate and helpful ones. You want to embrace positive thoughts that help you see the good in life and that allow you to feel joy.

When evaluating the accuracy and helpfulness of your thoughts, use the following questions to guide you toward a more realistic and helpful perspective:

- Is this thought necessarily true?

- Is this thought consistent with the evidence?

- What is the evidence for and against this thought?

- Are there other ways of thinking about the situation?

- Could there be an alternative explanation?

- How might someone else think about this situation?

- What might you say to someone else who was in this same situation?

- Are your thoughts helpful?

- Overall, is there another way to look at this situation?

Worksheet

EVALUATE YOUR THINKING

· · · · · ·

To get into the habit of evaluating your automatic thoughts, use this worksheet to ask yourself the following series of guided questions to determine the accuracy or helpfulness of your thoughts.

What was the specific situation?

_____

_____

_____

What automatic thought did you have about the situation?

_____

_____

_____

Is this thought necessarily true? Is it helpful?

_____

_____

_____

Is this thought consistent with the evidence?

_____

_____

_____

What is the evidence for this thought?

_____

_____

_____

What is the evidence against this thought?

_____

_____

_____

How might someone else think about this situation?

_____

_____

_____

What might you say to someone else who was in this same situation?

_____

_____

_____

Is there another way to look at this situation?

_____

_____

_____

What is an alternate thought that might be a more accurate and helpful way of thinking about the situation?

_____

_____

_____

 LEARNING

Every thought that pops into your head is not necessarily true. Rather than automatically accepting your thoughts at face value, you can learn to identify, evaluate, and modify your thoughts to reflect the most accurate and helpful perspective.

 PRACTICE

Over the next week, be on the lookout for negative or unhelpful thoughts as they arise. Whenever you experience one of these thoughts, write it down and go through the series of guided questions to uncover the truth.

 COPING REMINDER

• Thoughts are not facts. You don't have to blindly accept your thoughts as true.

• You are stronger than your thoughts.

REFRAME YOUR THINKING

In addition to looking at the evidence for and against your thoughts and considering alternate viewpoints, there are numerous ways to examine and reframe your thinking, such as pie charts, cost-benefit analyses, continuums, questioning utility, and acceptance.

Pie Charts

Pie charts are a useful tool to examine your thoughts when you are taking the blame or assuming full responsibility for something that has multiple contributing factors. These charts help you see the bigger picture so you don't place too much value on just one piece of the pie.

To illustrate, let's say that your child has been acting out at school and you've been putting the blame on yourself. By using a pie chart, you can look at all the other "slices" that might be contributing to this behavior. For example, perhaps your child is struggling because their classroom is too hot or overcrowded, or maybe they're being bullied or teased by their peers. It's also important to consider that your child may simply have problems with impulse control and would benefit from a different teaching style. They may also be acting out due to the messages they have internalized from the internet, television, books, music, or other adults in their life. All these factors can work together to cause your child to act out. With a visual representation, it's much easier to see that the blame cannot be squarely put on you alone.

Pie charts can also allow you to see yourself for who you are as a whole. For example, instead of defining yourself solely by your shape and size, you can consider the multitude of elements of "you" that make up each piece of the pie, such as your personality, interests, aptitudes, sense of humor, spirituality, kindness, and compassion. This can allow you to develop a more balanced perspective regarding your self-worth.

RESPONSIBILITY PIE

• • • • • •

Bring to mind a negative situation in your life that you are taking full responsibility for. Instead of allowing yourself to assume that you are 100 percent to blame, use this pie chart to consider whether other factors played a role.

Describe the situation you are blaming yourself for.

_____

_____

Make a list of all the people or factors that could have contributed to this situation too.

_____

_____

Now put each factor in the following pie chart, and assign each factor a percentage that reflects how responsible it is for this outcome. Make sure to also assign a percentage of responsibility to yourself, but keep in mind that if you listed other contributing factors, then you cannot be 100 percent to blame.

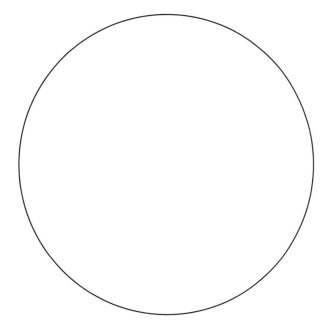

Once you've completed the pie chart, reassess how much fault lies in yourself. Is it less than you first thought? How much do you think you are to blame now?

_____

_____

_____

_____

LEARNING

Using a pie chart is a helpful way to recognize when you are not solely responsible for a specific situation. It gives you a big-picture viewpoint.

PRACTICE

The next time you take full responsibility for a situation that may not be all your fault, use the pie chart to help you see all the other factors involved. You can also use the pie chart whenever you are defining yourself on the basis of a single factor, such as your weight or appearance. The pie chart will help you visualize all the other elements that make you who you are, including your personality, interests, skills, and so on.

COPING REMINDER

• Don't automatically assume you are 100 percent to blame.

• Don't let one negative define everything.

Looking at a Continuum

Since depression can make you see situations in the most negative and extreme ways, another way to reframe your thoughts and gain a more realistic perspective is to look at things along a continuum. For example, consider a woman who thinks she is the worst friend of all time because she is always late, cancels plans, and is not readily available by phone or text. In order to reframe her thinking, she can create a continuum of being a friend that includes descriptions of the ideal friend, the good-but-not-ideal friend, the okay friend, the bad friend, and the absolute worst friend (where she has placed herself).

In describing the qualities of an "ideal" friend and a "good" friend, she might find out she has many of those same qualities. For example, an ideal and good friend might make the best intentions to show up at important events, call or text when someone is going through a tough a time, provide a shoulder to cry on, be loyal, and keep secrets—which are all characteristics that she embodies. Similarly, when she describes the qualities of a "bad" friend or the "absolute worst" friend—for example, someone who steals from, insults, or outright betrays their friends—she might realize that she is not the worst friend after all. In turn, she can recognize that she has judged herself too harshly and might fall on the continuum closer to an ideal friend than she previously thought.

You can apply this same logic to any negative thoughts that are causing you distress. By using a continuum, you can better see the nuances of the situation and come to a more balanced perspective.

CONTINUUM PERSPECTIVE

• • • • • •

Think of time when you judged yourself harshly and immediately assumed the worst-case scenario. Perhaps you told yourself you were unlikeable, unattractive, or incompetent. To create a more accurate and helpful point of view, consider the opposite of that quality (e.g., likeable, attractive, competent). Think of the virtues that make up that concept. For example, someone who is smart might be a good problem solver, do well on tests, and think outside the box, while someone who is likeable might be kind, caring, and a good listener. An example is provided for you first, followed by a blank continuum for your own situation.

EXAMPLE:

State the negative belief: _I am the worst employee._
Identify three components that an employee would be judged on:

#1: _Arriving on time_

Never on time	Late most of the time	Late sometimes	Occasionally late	Late once	Always on time
		X			

#2: _Relationship with coworkers_

Fights with other employees	Yells a lot	Often rude	Civil	Gets along with most people	Gets along with everyone
					X

#3: _Feedback on yearly review_

Lots of negative feedback	Some negative feedback	Neutral feedback	Some positive feedback	Mostly positive	Rave reviews
				X	

With this new perspective, do you now see yourself differently? What is a more realistic and helpful way of looking at things?
I am far from being the worst employee. My being tardy sometimes doesn't negate the other positive data I receive in the workplace.

YOUR TURN:

State the negative belief: _____

Identify three components that a _____ (e.g., friend, parent, employee, partner, etc.) would be judged on:

#1: _____

| Most negative | Less negative | Somewhat negative | Somewhat positive | More positive | Most positive |

#2: _____

| Most negative | Less negative | Somewhat negative | Somewhat positive | More positive | Most positive |

#3: _____

| Most negative | Less negative | Somewhat negative | Somewhat positive | More positive | Most positive |

With this new perspective, do you now see yourself differently? What is a more realistic and helpful way of looking at things?

_____

_____

_____

_____

_____

LEARNING

When you focus on any one negative quality, you can blow things out of proportion and fail to see yourself accurately. The continuum analysis is an opportunity to factually evaluate your qualities, which enables you to see yourself in the most positive and accurate way possible.

PRACTICE

The next time you consider yourself the *worst* anything—friend, worker, athlete, partner, parent, sibling—look at yourself on a continuum and reconsider your initial rating. Pay attention to the positive information.

COPING REMINDER

- You are probably not the worst and may in fact be much closer to being the best.
- Pay attention to what the objective facts say instead of letting your feelings run the show.

Questioning Utility

Sometimes people can get caught in patterns of thinking that are unhelpful, even if the thoughts themselves are true or partially true. In this case, the goal is not to negate or challenge the automatic thought, but to learn to look at it in a way that doesn't let it bother you as much. The question to ask yourself is "While this thought may be true, is it useful to think this way?" or "What purpose does it serve me to continue to talk about this?" By considering the utility of the thought, you can view the situation in a more helpful way.

For example, let's say that you're unhappy with your current job position, so you're looking at potential job postings online. You come across one that seems too good to be true, but you tell yourself, "I won't get this job anyway." While it is possible you won't get the job, telling yourself this ahead of time will just make you feel defeated. Furthermore, it may prevent you from acting in ways to maximize your chances of getting the job, such as applying in the first place. Similarly, let's say you just got the results of your board exam back and you found out you failed. In response, you tell yourself "I'm never going to pass this exam." While you may have failed the first time (and you may fail again), this automatic thought can ignite a self-fulfilling prophecy that prevents you from even trying again.

These unhelpful thoughts diminish your self-confidence and block you from your goals. Instead, you can replace the thoughts with more helpful ones, such as "I can't know that I won't get this job until it happens. Until then, I will keep trying" or "I flunked the board exam, but that doesn't mean I can't take it again."

QUESTION THE HELPFULNESS OF YOUR THINKING

• • • • • •

Whenever you find yourself caught in a pattern of negative thinking, consider whether there is any utility in continuing to dwell on this thought (even if the thought is true or at least partially true). Ask yourself whether there are any advantages to having this thought or whether it just brings you down.

What is the thought that you find yourself stuck in?

_____

_____

_____

_____

How does this thought affect you?

_____

_____

_____

_____

Does this thought help you or hurt you?

_____

_____

_____

_____

Does this thought get you closer to or further from your goals?

_____

_____

_____

_____

What is a more helpful way to think about this?

_____

_____

_____

_____

LEARNING

Even thoughts that are true (or partially true) can drive distress and get in your way. Questioning the utility of the thought (e.g., "Is it helpful to think this way?") and considering alternative, more helpful viewpoints can keep you moving forward.

PRACTICE

The next time something doesn't go your way and you get caught in an unhelpful thought, ask yourself whether it serves any purpose to continue dwelling on the thought. If it doesn't, brainstorm at least two other more helpful ways of looking at the situation.

COPING REMINDER

- Helpful thoughts rally you to effective action.
- You can squash your unhelpful thoughts.

Triple A's of Effectiveness

Since depression clouds your judgment, it can lead you to feel hopeless and assume that things will never get better. You allow negative events to mean more than they do, which can lead you to predict future calamity and disaster. In these cases, you can reframe your thinking by using the triple A's of effectiveness: acknowledge, accept, and take appropriate action.

The first "A" simply involves **acknowledging** the facts of the situation. For example, perhaps you receive an abnormal medical result, you don't get your dream job, you do poorly on a school assignment, or your partner breaks up with you. With acknowledgment, you simply record the objective facts as they are. The second step is to practice **acceptance**, in which you reserve judgments—instead of exaggerating the situation—and draw conclusions based solely on the facts. For example, instead of telling yourself "I am going to die," "I will never get a job," "I am going to flunk out of school," or "I will never find love again," you ask yourself what the facts tell you. In the case of your medical test, you may consider many explanations for the results, including many that are highly treatable.

This nonjudgmental perspective allows you to make a plan that is most effective and appropriate for the situation, which leads you to the third step: **action**. Here you brainstorm what you can do or say to address the problem or work toward your goal. For example, you might schedule an appointment with your doctor and follow through on any recommended tests, apply for more jobs, talk to your teacher about receiving extra credit, or sign up for dating apps when you feel ready to put yourself out there again. When you use the triple A's of effectiveness, you do not allow yourself to feel powerless when addressing a distressing situation.

USE THE 3 A'S TO THINK EFFECTIVELY

• • • • • •

The next time you jump to conclusions or give unnecessary meaning to negative events in your life, use the triple A's to think more effectively: <u>A</u>cknowledge the facts, practice <u>A</u>cceptance by taking a nonjudgmental attitude, and take appropriate <u>A</u>ction.

Acknowledge the facts:

Record the specifics of the situation. What are the objective facts?

_____

_____

_____

_____

_____

_____

Accept without judgment:

Instead of exaggerating the meaning of the situation or making future predictions, draw accurate conclusions based on the facts. What do the facts tell you?

_____

_____

_____

_____

_____

_____

Act appropriately:

Instead of using ineffective compensatory strategies, like avoidance or poor communication, brainstorm the steps you need to take to address the situation. What are some appropriate actions you can take?

_____

_____

_____

_____

_____

_____

_____

LEARNING

Instead of jumping to conclusions when negative events happen, you can reserve judgment until you have the facts and then take action by following up with the most appropriate next steps.

PRACTICE

To get into the habit of using the triple A's, practice with a friend or family member by helping them see things in a more objective way the next time they get upset by a negative experience. Help them acknowledge the facts, not blow things out of proportion, and keep moving forward in a way that is effective.

COPING REMINDER

• Whatever happens, you can handle it.

• Things happen—roll with it.

THOUGHT REGISTER

A thought register is a good way to put together everything you've learned so far about capturing, identifying, and reframing your thoughts. You can view a thought register as a sort of road map—you will travel all the way from your initial reaction to an event, through the different thoughts you have about it, and finally arrive at a reframed response with more accurate, unbiased thoughts.

The first part of a thought register involves thinking about a specific situation or event that bothered you. Make note of the event and record what specific automatic thoughts, emotions, and body responses you experienced at the time, as well as what behaviors you engaged in. Next, identify the doubt labels, assumptions, or thinking errors that may be relevant to how you viewed that situation. Remember that doubt labels reflect the nasty names you call yourself when you feel insecure, whereas assumptions are "if/then" statements that underlie doubt labels and that guide your behavior. Thinking errors are overall patterns of irrational thinking.

Finally, reframe your thinking by looking at the evidence and considering different perspectives. With this more accurate or helpful view of the situation, notice if you detect a difference in your feelings, body responses, and behaviors. Altogether, this information should help you see that your self-doubt label was biasing your viewpoint and may not have been 100 percent true.

Worksheet

THOUGHT REGISTER

• • • • • •

Think about a recent event that caused you a lot of distress. Record the situation and all your thoughts, feelings, and behaviors that you had at the time. Then, use the skills you've gained to reframe those thoughts into a more accurate and helpful response. An example is provided for you here, followed by a blank chart for you to fill in on your own.

Situation	Automatic Thoughts	Doubt Label	Assumptions	Thinking Errors	Reframe Your Thinking
I had a doctor's appointment to discuss my diagnosis and was told there are no precise answers to my disease at this time.	I'm a ticking time bomb. It's my fault.	I am irresponsible. I am powerless.	If bad things happen, then I am responsible.	Zooming in on the negative: I'm focusing on the days in my youth (when I had a drink or two too many) and inappropriately taking blame.	I am powerless against the disease being there, but I am not powerless to do all I can to address it—and I am doing just that.
	Emotions			Catastrophizing: Just because I have a disease doesn't mean it's a death sentence.	**Response**
	Fear, shame, nervousness				I feel calmer, I'm no longer nauseous, and I can stop worrying and do everything I need to take care of my body but not let it stop me from fully living life now. I am the opposite of irresponsible and do have power.
	Body Response			Extreme thinking: Getting sick is not completely under my control. I do plenty to try to be healthy.	
	Nauseous, shaky				
	Behavior				
	Worrying, checking the internet, crying, seeking reassurance from loved ones				

Situation	Automatic Thoughts	Doubt Label	Assumptions	Thinking Errors	Reframe Your Thinking
	Emotions				Response
	Body Response				
	Behavior				

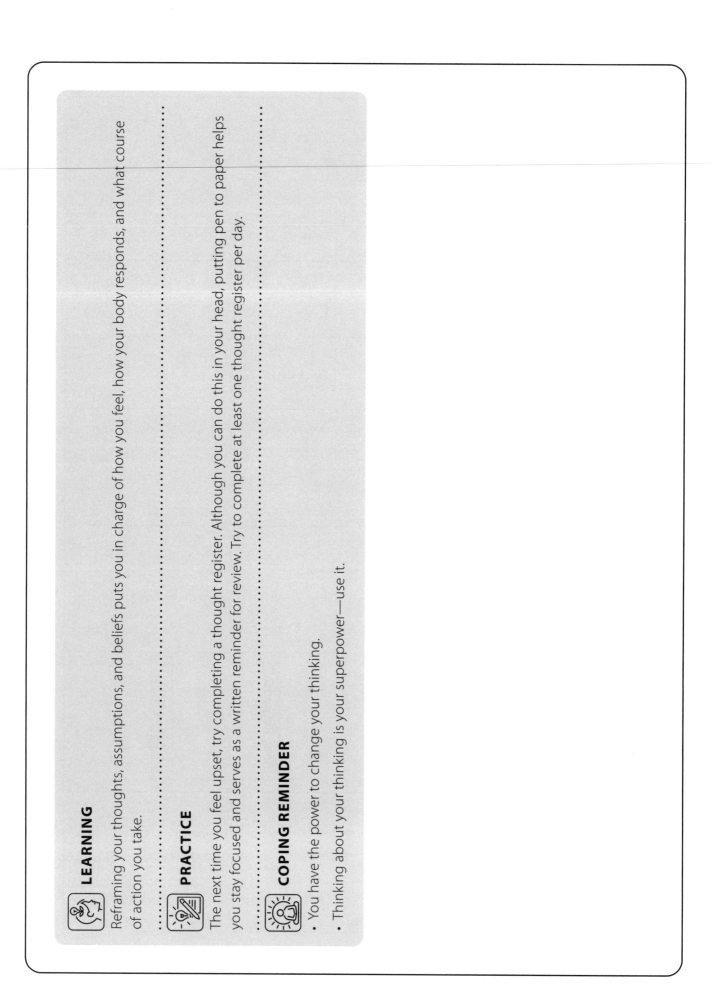

LEARNING

Reframing your thoughts, assumptions, and beliefs puts you in charge of how you feel, how your body responds, and what course of action you take.

PRACTICE

The next time you feel upset, try completing a thought register. Although you can do this in your head, putting pen to paper helps you stay focused and serves as a written reminder for review. Try to complete at least one thought register per day.

COPING REMINDER

- You have the power to change your thinking.
- Thinking about your thinking is your superpower—use it.

⬡ 5

ANXIETY

UNDERSTANDING ANXIETY

The experience of anxiety is a reality of the human condition. It is nature's way of preparing us to face threatening or dangerous situations by pumping adrenaline into our bodies, which makes us feel alert and gives us the energy we need to address the challenges ahead. Leslie's experience with anxiety during a travel-related complication can help to illustrate this point:

Upon landing in Dallas International Airport, my phone alerted me that my connecting flight to my vacation destination was canceled, and my new flight was booked for three days later. Energy began coursing throughout my body, and my brain started focusing on how to address the problem. I swung into action, grabbing my belongings and rushing off the plane to find the nearest customer service agent while simultaneously dialing airline customer service on my phone. Meanwhile, my husband sauntered along while he commiserated on the phone with some of our friends who were on another flight.

As I rushed to the customer service counter, I noticed how physically anxious I felt. My mouth was dry, my muscles were tense, my previous hunger was gone, and I was breathing as if I had just run an Olympic race. The automated telephone recording told me I would be on hold for 50 minutes, and seeing as the customer service line was a mile long, I proceeded to run out of the terminal to find my way to the check-in counter instead. The helpful agent maneuvered us onto a flight to LAX for later that day, but it had an unreasonably short connection time, so she also booked us on a backup flight at the crack of dawn the next day.

With time to kill, we grabbed some lunch, and I quickly noticed that once I had food in my system, my body started to calm down—I knew that we now had a plan. When we landed in Los Angeles with no possibility of making our connection, we made our way to customer service, confirmed our flight for the next day, obtained our hotel vouchers, and headed out to make the best of our overnight layover. Checking in at dawn for our flight the next day, the agent was concerned about our bags since they should have been claimed rather than transferred to this flight, but she did what she could to remedy the situation. I sat calmly at the gate, while my husband anxiously worried about our bags making it to our destination.

Once our plane was in the air, I started to reflect on this experience. I realized how mindfully aware of my anxiety I had been the day before and how appreciative I was of how energized and alert it made me feel. How it allowed my problem-solving skills to fully engage. How my brain knew the danger of not getting to our destination. How sitting at the gate the next day, my lack of concern over our bags didn't activate me like it did my husband. I wasn't calm because it wouldn't be a hassle—it probably would be—but if our bags didn't make it in time, it wouldn't be the end of the world. The bags would either arrive or they wouldn't, and nothing I could do or say at that moment would change that. I don't usually observe my own anxiety, but having just been interviewed on the topic the previous day, it was at the front of my mind.

DO YOU HAVE ANXIETY?

Think of how you might face Leslie's travel situation. Instead of taking advantage of the adrenaline rush and using it to act quickly and problem solve the situation, you might have given the physical symptoms of anxiety most of your attention, causing it to grow your discomfort, distract you, or prevent you from effectively dealing with the problem at hand. Recall that anxiety is the body's natural way of mobilizing us to take action in response to some perceived threat or challenge at hand. When faced with a real issue, such as a canceled flight, anxiety is a helpful response that mobilizes us to action. Without anxiety, we would have much more difficulty in moving, performing, or solving issues.

Therefore, anxiety is not the problem; it is the *fear* of anxiety that makes it a problem. When you fear arousal, you magnify the physical symptoms of anxiety by focusing on them. As a result, you make efforts to suppress the anxiety, which interferes with your ability to address the stressor at hand. In the process of suppressing this anxiety, you may start trying to avoid the people, situations, or experiences that elicit any symptoms of anxiety, which only serves to magnify your fears and make it harder to face them. Problems also arise when you exaggerate the threat or underestimate your ability to cope with it, causing you to always assume the worst-case scenario will occur. For example, if you flunk a test, you assume that you'll never graduate. Or if you get rejected on a first date, you assume you'll never find love.

However, when you believe that you can handle whatever is thrown your way, the fear of anxiety diminishes. When Leslie's flight was canceled, she knew it was a problem that could be solved, which allowed her anxiety to be helpful. However, if she had overestimated the danger and underestimated her ability to cope, then her anxiety would have become problematic. To see if anxiety is a problem for you, fill out the following two worksheets. The first worksheet gauges the extent to which anxiety symptoms are interfering with your life, and the second will help you begin to understand that anxiety in and of itself is nothing to fear.*

GENERALIZED ANXIETY DISORDER QUESTIONNAIRE (GAD-7)*

• • • • • •

If you have been feeling anxious or on edge lately, this tool can help you evaluate the severity of your anxiety. However, it is not intended to take the place of a professional diagnosis.

Over the last two weeks, how often have you been bothered by any of the following problems?

Not at all	Several days	More than half the days	Nearly every day
0	1	2	3

_____ 1. Feeling nervous, anxious, or on edge

_____ 2. Not being able to stop or control worrying

_____ 3. Worrying too much about different things

_____ 4. Trouble relaxing

_____ 5. Being so restless that it is hard to sit still

_____ 6. Becoming easily annoyed or irritable

_____ 7. Feeling afraid, as if something awful might happen

_____ **Total score**

If you checked off *any* problem on this questionnaire, how *difficult* have these problems made it for you to do your work, take care of things at home, or get along with other people?

☐ Not difficult at all   ☐ Somewhat difficult   ☐ Very difficult   ☐ Extremely difficult

* The GAD-7 was developed by Drs. Robert L. Spitzer, Janet B.W. Williams, Kurt Kroenke and colleagues, with an educational grant from Pfizer Inc. No permission required to reproduce, translate, display, or distribute.

LEARNING

This inventory helped you take your anxiety temperature. You can interpret your scores with the following guidelines:

Minimal anxiety	0–4
Mild anxiety	5–9
Moderate anxiety	10–14
Severe anxiety	15–21

It is important to know that anxiety can affect you whether your symptoms are minimal or severe. When you allow anxiety to take control and view it as something to fear, you choose ineffective behavioral strategies and it becomes hard to function.

. . . .

 PRACTICE

Every two weeks, do a mental health check-in by measuring your anxiety symptoms again, and see whether the principles you are putting into practice are working.

. . . .

 COPING REMINDER

• Anxiety is not dangerous.
• Anxiety itself is not a problem; it is your fear surrounding the anxiety that is the problem.

UNDERSTANDING YOUR FEAR OF ANXIETY

• • • • • •

Although you may believe that anxiety is dangerous—and that the goal of treatment should be to eliminate all anxiety from your life—it is important to adjust your expectations. Rarely does everything in life always go as planned. There will always be challenges and roadblocks along the way. And as you've learned, not only is anxiety a completely normal human response in these situations, but it can even be helpful. It alerts you that there is something wrong that needs your attention. Use this worksheet to help you understand that anxiety is nothing to fear.

Consider these common concerns about anxiety. Are any of them true for you?

T or F   My anxiety will never go away.

T or F   My anxiety will keep getting worse.

T or F   My anxiety will harm me physically.

T or F   My anxiety will make me unable to function.

T or F   My anxiety will make me less appealing.

What else about anxiety scares you? What are you afraid will happen?

_____

_____

_____

_____

_____

_____

_____

_____

To determine if your fears about anxiety are true, run an experiment to test your predictions. First, stand up and take rapid, shallow breaths for 60 seconds (you can stop after 30 seconds if it becomes too much for you). Observe how anxious you feel afterward and describe the symptoms you are experiencing.

_____

_____

_____

_____

_____

Then sit down, close your mouth, and breathe in and out of your nose as slowly and evenly as possible for three breath cycles. On the third breath, part your lips when you exhale. Once again, observe your anxiety and describe what you are experiencing.

_____

_____

_____

_____

_____

If you're still physically uncomfortable, pick up a book and quietly read any paragraph backward. Notice how anxious you feel now. Did your prediction come true? Did your anxiety get worse? Last forever? Harm you in any way?

_____

_____

_____

_____

_____

_____

LEARNING

Although anxiety can be an unpleasant experience, it is not dangerous. In this exercise, you purposely practiced hyperventilating for one minute, which activated your anxiety response. However, when you stopped hyperventilating—and instead practiced deep breathing and a distraction technique—your body gradually returned to normal. In doing so, you learned that anxiety is not dangerous, nor does it last forever. If the anxiety had been medically dangerous, it would not have gone away like it did. Most importantly, no matter how uncomfortable the anxiety is, there is no need to do anything at all if you accept that anxiety is not dangerous.

 PRACTICE

Repeat this exercise at least three times a day until you no longer fear your anxiety symptoms. Then broaden your experiment: Try hyperventilating until you notice symptoms of anxiety, and then test out whether you can function. For example, try to carry on a conversation, add up a column of numbers, tie your shoes, read a sentence, or drill in a screw. Eventually, you might even see the anxiety go away on its own without needing to use deep breathing or distraction techniques. You'll find that regardless of how you respond, the symptoms will eventually disappear.

 COPING REMINDER

- Anxiety is uncomfortable, but it is not harmful.
- Anxiety can't hurt you—and it will go away!
- You can function even if you are anxious.

THE PROBABILITY ERROR AND THE CATASTROPHIC ERROR

When people are anxious, they tend to overestimate the likelihood that something bad will happen, which is known as the probability error. For example, someone with social anxiety may assume that everyone at an upcoming party will find them boring and not want to talk to them. A person with panic disorder will predict that their physical symptoms of dizziness, racing heart, and sweating will worsen and lead to an inevitable panic attack. The probability error is also common among people with intrusive thoughts, who falsely believe that simply having these thoughts increases the likelihood that they will come true. For example, someone with intrusive thoughts of opening the emergency exit door on a plane may fear that they will act on this thought if they are seated in the exit row.

Not only do people with anxiety overestimate the probability of negative outcomes, but they also overestimate how severe those negative outcomes will be. This is known as the catastrophic error, and it reflects the belief that negative outcomes will always involve the worst-case scenario. For example, the person with social anxiety may believe it will be the end of the world if other attendees at the party find them boring, and they will never be able to face those people again. Similarly, someone experiencing symptoms of a panic attack may assume that these symptoms are evidence of an impending heart attack or death, when the reality is these symptoms are unpleasant but not medically dangerous.

Instead of accepting these predictions as facts, you can learn to evaluate both the probability and consequences of your fears coming true by asking yourself several questions that help you objectively evaluate those ideas:

- What is the worst, best, and most likely outcome?

- Could you survive the worst outcome if it happened?

- Has your feared outcome ever happened? If so, when?

- Do you know what is going to happen? Or is it just a possibility?

- Are your thoughts necessarily true? Or is it possible that you are wrong?

- Are these thoughts helpful?

- Are these thoughts consistent with the evidence?

- What might you say to a friend who was having these thoughts?

- What are the facts?

- Are there other possibilities?

- Where did you get this idea to begin with? Is it a valid source?

COUNTERING THE PROBABILITY ERROR AND THE CATASTROPHIC ERROR

• • • • • •

When we get anxious, we tend to overestimate both the probability that something bad will happen, as well as the consequences of it. Learning to question the accuracy of your thinking can eliminate anxiety that comes from exaggerated perceptions of threat. In this exercise, you'll describe your feared outcome, consider how likely this outcome is, and determine whether your feared consequence would be as catastrophic as you imagined. An example is provided for you first, followed by space for you to fill in your own.

EXAMPLE:

1. What do you fear will happen?
   I will mispronounce a word during my presentation and make a fool of myself.

2. Is this concern likely to happen, a given, or a remote possibility?
   I might mispronounce a word, but I have been practicing, so it is highly unlikely.

3. Has this ever happened to you before?
   I did stumble over a couple of words at my last presentation, but I was able to keep going with the presentation, and no one treated me any differently after the fact.

4. If this feared outcome happens, what is the best, worst, and most likely outcome?

   • Worst outcome: Everyone will notice and think less of me forever.

   • Best outcome: No one will notice if I do mispronounce a word.

   • Most likely outcome: Some people will notice but not think less of me.

5. Could you survive the worst outcome if it happened? Would it be the end of the world?
   Even if some people think less of me, it would not impact my life in any significant way.

6. What is a more accurate view of the probability and consequences?
   Realistically, most people are not paying close enough attention to notice if I mispronounce a word. But on the rare possibility they do, so what? It is not going to be the problem I imagined.

YOUR TURN:

1. What do you fear will happen?

_____

_____

_____

2. Is this concern likely to happen, a given, or a remote possibility?

_____

_____

_____

3. Has this ever happened to you before?

_____

_____

_____

4. If this feared outcome happens, what is the best, worst, and most likely outcome?

- Worst outcome: _____

_____

_____

- Best outcome: _____

_____

_____

- Most likely outcome: _____

_____

_____

5. Could you survive the worst outcome if it happened? Would it be the end of the world?

_____

_____

_____

6. What is a more accurate view of the probability and consequences?

_____

_____

_____

LEARNING

Anxiety has a tendency to make you overestimate the probability that bad things will happen, as well as how bad those outcomes will be. You can reduce anxiety by examining the likelihood of your feared outcome and considering that the consequences may not be as disastrous as imagined.

PRACTICE

The next time you feel anxious, think about the potential outcome of the situation. Ask yourself if you are overestimating the probability or severity of this outcome. Are you imagining a danger that isn't there at all or that is exaggerated? Use the questions in this worksheet to help you examine the accuracy of your anxious thoughts.

COPING REMINDER

- Possibilities are not probabilities.
- Just because something bad happens doesn't mean it will result in dire consequences.

THE RESOURCE ERROR

In addition to the probability error and the catastrophic error, there's a third error associated with anxiety: the resource error. What this means is that when you get anxious, you often fail to see your ability to cope. You do this by underestimating the resources you have within and outside of yourself. Internal resources include those qualities, skills, and talents that you always carry with you, such as self-confidence, humor, smarts, problem-solving skills, faith, and hope. When we use these types of resources to manage anxiety, symptoms can diminish quicker, and distress can even show up with less severity. External resources include people in your community who can come to your aid when issues arise, such as therapists, medical professionals, first responders, neighbors, family, friends, colleagues, and good Samaritans. When you're able to recognize the resources you have on hand, you'll feel more confident to handle any threats or challenges that arise (or are likely to arise).

IDENTIFY YOUR INTERNAL AND EXTERNAL RESOURCES

· · · · · ·

We all have abilities, skills, knowledge, allies, and support systems that equip us to handle any stressors that life throws our way—yourself included. When the going gets tough, use this worksheet to identify the internal and external resources available to you.

Internal Resources

Look through the list of attributes and skills listed here, and circle all the resources that you carry within yourself.

Skills & Knowledge

Attention to detail	Multitasking	Technology
Budgeting	Problem-solving	Time management
Communication	Researching	Troubleshooting
Critical thinking	Selling	Working under pressure
Leadership	Storytelling	Writing
Listening	Studying	Other: _____
Negotiation	Supervising	Other: _____
Mathematics	Teamwork	Other: _____

Qualities

Accepting	Focused	Organized
Adaptable	Generous	Punctual
Articulate	Hardworking	Patient
Brave	Honest	Responsible
Caring	Imaginative	Thorough
Determined	Intelligent	Other: _____
Energetic	Motivated	Other: _____
Flexible	Open-minded	Other: _____

How have these internal resources helped you overcome obstacles in the past?

_____

_____

_____

External Resources

Here are some possible external resources that could help you face a challenging situation. Circle any resources that have helped you in the past or that could help you in the future:

Accountant	Good Samaritan	Plumber
Coach	Lawyer	Police
Coworker	Lifeguard	Sober coach
Dentist	Maintenance worker	Supervisor
Electrician	Medical professional	Teacher
Family	Mental health provider	Other: _____
Friend	Neighbor	Other: _____
Fire department	Physical therapist	Other: _____

LEARNING

When you feel ill-equipped to handle threatening or challenging situations, anxiety can take control. But when you know you're armed with internal and external resources, you'll feel more prepared to face the day and conquer your fears.

 PRACTICE

Jot down each of your resources on a sticky note, and place these notes around your home. Every time you walk by a note, mindfully read it and maybe even voice your resource out loud. Remind yourself of your strengths as often as possible.

 COPING REMINDER

- You have overcome challenges before.
- You are strong enough to face any situation.
- You can always ask someone for support.
- Bring your team—whether they are physically with you or not, you have allies to help.

RISK/RESOURCE RATIO

Now that you've learned about the three errors that can contribute to anxiety—the probability error, the catastrophic error, and the resource error—let's put together what you've learned so anxiety doesn't get the best of you. Anxiety can lead to unnecessary worry, in which you repeatedly replay the same feared scenario in your mind, over and over again, without taking action. For example, you might be consumed with persistent, nagging fears of negative outcomes that could happen in the future, like "What if I flunk my test?" "What if there is traffic and I miss my connection?" or "What if my child gets into an accident?"

Although worry can masquerade as problem-solving in these situations—as if giving attention to these fears will prevent them from happening—it doesn't actually do anything to solve the problem. Instead, it drives fear, makes you physically uncomfortable, induces stress, fatigues you, wastes time, prevents you from being present, and compromises your ability to experience pleasure. The same is true when you worry about past events. You have no power to change what has already taken place, so replaying these events in your mind does nothing except deplete your energy.

Instead of worrying, it is important to learn to evaluate your concerns and take appropriate action if possible. To do so, you want to look at your risk/resource ratio, which involves comparing (1) the risk of actual threat with (2) your resources or ability to cope. Here are the steps involved in this process:

1. When you find yourself experiencing anxiety, ask yourself what you are afraid of. What are you concerned is going to happen (and what will be the consequences if it does)?

2. Then ask yourself how accurate your estimations are. Is the concern likely to happen, a remote possibility, or an impossibility?

3. If what you are concerned about is very *unlikely* to happen or downright impossible (or even if it did happen, the consequences would *not* be problematic at all), then it is unnecessary to imagine how you would cope. In this case, remind yourself that wasting your energy worrying about an imaginary problem only distracts you from being present.

4. However, if what you are concerned about is *possible* or *likely* to happen (and the consequences *would* be problematic), then it is important to gather your resources in preparation for battle. Even if you are facing a real challenge, when you know that you have the resources to handle it, you won't feel as anxious. You can then use your resources to come up with a plan to address the situation.

YOUR RISK/RESOURCE RATIO

• • • • • •

Use these questions to analyze your risk/resource ratio. By learning to estimate the presence of true danger more accurately—and spending your time problem-solving only when danger is a real possibility—you won't let anxiety and worry take control. An example is provided for you first, followed by space for you to examine your own risk/resource ratio.

EXAMPLE:

1. Describe a situation that makes you anxious.
   You get a ticket for going 20 mph over the speed limit.

2. What are you afraid of? What are you concerned is going to happen (and what will be the consequences if it does)?
   I am going to get a ton of points, I will lose my license for six months, and my insurance rate will increase significantly.

3. Question the accuracy of your concerns. Is the concern likely to happen, a remote possibility, or an impossibility?
   All of these consequences are possible and likely to happen since I was going significantly over the speed limit.

4. What internal and external resources do you have to face this situation? Is there an action plan you can put into place?
   I have years of a good driving record, so I might be able to reduce the consequences. I can consult with a ticket clinic or a lawyer to see if they can help. I can also go to court and fight my case directly. Other people I know have had their consequences reduced, so it's possible I might have that result too. Even if the worst thing happened, I could survive without my car for six months, use a ride service, ride my bike, or have my partner drive me. Although my insurance rate may go up, it will only be temporary since with another period of no infractions, it will reduce again.

5. Now reflect on the risks and resources. What is a realistic appraisal of this threat, and are you prepared to face it?
   The odds that there will be some consequences for my speeding are fairly high, but if I take action, it may not be the worst-case scenario. Even if the worst thing happened (e.g., losing my license for six months), it will be temporary, I have options, and I will get through it.

YOUR TURN:

1. Describe a situation that makes you anxious.

_____

_____

_____

_____

_____

2. What are you afraid of? What are you concerned is going to happen (and what will be the consequences if it does)?

_____

_____

_____

_____

3. Question the accuracy of your concerns. Is the concern likely to happen, a remote possibility, or an impossibility?

_____

_____

_____

_____

4. What internal and external resources do you have to face this situation? Is there an action plan you can put into place?

_____

_____

_____

_____

_____

5. Now reflect on the risks and resources. What is a realistic appraisal of this threat, and are you prepared to face it?

_____

_____

_____

_____

LEARNING

Worrying doesn't prevent bad things from happening—it just tortures you. Instead of worrying about the past or the future, examine the probability of your feared outcome. If your fear is likely to come true, then actively put your efforts into problem-solving.

PRACTICE

The next time you find yourself worrying or having persistent what-if thoughts, try to purposely imagine that the worst-case scenario comes to fruition. Then imagine using your resources to survive it.

COPING REMINDER

- Worry keeps you from doing what matters or having joy.

- You don't have to figure out every solution ahead of time. If difficulty arises, you can problem solve at that time.

QUIET YOUR MIND AND RAISE YOUR THRESHOLD

• • • • • •

When worry gets the best of you, your mind obsesses over the past or the future. Those persistent nagging thoughts are hard to turn off and can interfere with your ability to be engaged in the present moment. The following exercise is a way to quiet your mind and relax your body, making you less reactive and raising your arousal threshold. Consider making a recording of this script so you can listen to it whenever you want to quiet your mind and relax your body. However, with practice, you will be able to follow the instructions without the script.

To begin, find a quiet place, either sitting comfortably with your shoes off and legs out straight in front of you or lying down. Then close your eyes and remove your glasses if you are wearing any. Take a nice, slow breath in through your nose, and exhale as slowly as possible through your mouth. Continue to breathe slowly and evenly, in through the nose and out thorough the mouth, as you start the exercise:

Picture the color red and think to yourself the number 7.

Picture red and think 7.

Picture red and think 7.

Keep breathing, and as you exhale, think *relax, relax, relax.*

Now picture the color orange and think to yourself the number 6.

Picture orange and think 6.

Picture orange and think 6.

Keep breathing, and as you exhale, think *relax, relax, relax.*

Now picture the color yellow and think to yourself the number 5.

Picture yellow and think 5.

Picture yellow and think 5.

Keep breathing, and as you exhale, think *relax, relax, relax.*

Now picture the color green and think to yourself the number 4.

Picture green and think 4.

Picture green and think 4.

Keep breathing, and as you exhale, think relax, relax, relax.

Now picture the color blue and think to yourself the number 3.

Picture blue and think 3.

Picture blue and think 3.

Keep breathing, and as you exhale, think relax, relax, relax.

Now picture the color indigo and think to yourself the number 2.

Picture indigo and think 2.

Picture indigo and think 2.

Keep breathing, and as you exhale, think relax, relax, relax.

Now picture the color violet and think to yourself the number 1.

Picture violet and think 1.

Picture violet and think 1.

Keep breathing, and as you exhale, think *relax, relax, relax.*

If you are doing this exercise at bedtime, you can let yourself dose off, but if you are using it as a tool to face your day, then continue with the following prompts.

You are now going to count forward to 7.

Keep your eyes closed until you reach 7.

1… 2… 3… you are becoming more aware of your surroundings.

4… 5… you are becoming more alert but are still calm, peaceful, and relaxed.

6… 7… snap your fingers and open your eyes.

Notice how you feel.

LEARNING

A clear mind and calm body can help you face life's challenges. The goal is to be calm, relaxed, and clearheaded but alert and ready to function.

. . . .

 PRACTICE

You can also work with a partner and take turns reading the script to each other so you can both benefit from the experience of this hypnotic mindful relaxation.

. . . .

 COPING REMINDER

- You can quiet your mind and turn off your worry.
- A quiet mind and calm body fortify you to better handle any threat.

FACING YOUR FEARS

By working to counteract the probability, catastrophic, and resource errors, you've been laying the foundation for the next step in addressing your anxiety, which involves facing your fears in real time. Although the previous cognitive restructuring work you did is an important part of treatment, it is usually not sufficient to get fully unstuck from anxiety.

To free yourself from anxiety, you need to expose yourself to the very things that you fear. This is known as *exposure*, and it gives you an opportunity to test your fear hypothesis by seeing if your feared predictions—those worst-case scenarios and consequences you've thought about—really do come true. Without testing your predictions, the "what-ifs" of an unknown situation will always remain in the back of your mind. Exposure is a powerful tool because in most cases, your brain will learn that it was wrong in assuming the worst of the worst.

There are many different types of exposure that you can do, including in vivo, imaginal, virtual reality, and interoceptive exposure. In vivo exposure just means that you confront the source of your anxiety in real life. For example, if you are afraid to drive on a highway, ride in an elevator, or hold an insect, you do just that. Imaginal exposure takes place in your mind, meaning that you utilize all your senses to imagine yourself in the feared situation as realistically as possible. Virtual reality exposure involves the use of technology to create a simulation of your fear, whether it's flying in a plane or looking over the edge of a high building. Finally, interoceptive exposure involves intentionally exposing yourself to the feared bodily sensations associated with anxiety, such as dizziness, sweating, or breathlessness.

Although exposures can be uncomfortable and even frightening in the moment—since you're confronting the very source of your anxiety—it's important to keep in mind that this discomfort is only temporary. In the long run, facing your fears will allow you to overcome any problematic anxiety that is holding you back. It lets you learn that you can handle whatever comes your way.

IT MAKES SENSE TO FACE MY FEARS

• • • • • •

When you continue to avoid the situations, activities, or people that you are afraid of, you allow anxiety to win. This prevents you from doing the things you want, achieving your goals, and finding joy. It also prevents your brain from experiencing new learning because you never get an opportunity to test whether your feared predictions are wrong. Facing your fears is the only way to overcome crippling anxiety. To determine whether it makes sense to face your fears, make a list of all the advantages and disadvantages of facing your fears, as well as *not* facing them.

	Advantages	Disadvantages
Facing your fears		
Not facing your fears		

Once you've listed all the advantages and disadvantages of facing (or not facing) your fears, tally up the number of items in each quadrant. How do the advantages and disadvantages compare? Does it make sense to work on facing your fears?

_____

_____

_____

_____

_____

_____

_____

_____

_____

LEARNING

Although facing your fears may come at a small price, the rewards you will gain far outweigh that price. It makes sense to face your fears.

PRACTICE

Whenever doubt creeps in and tries to get in your way of doing exposure work, remind yourself of all the reasons you are doing it. For every disadvantage that comes to mind, see if you can come up with at least two advantages that reinforce the importance of facing your fears.

COPING REMINDER

- The only way to overcome anxiety is to face the very thing you fear.
- The discomfort of exposure work will be temporary—in the long run, you'll be free.

MAKING A FEAR HIERARCHY

When working to confront the very things you fear, sometimes it is easier to take baby steps rather than jumping in headfirst. To do so, you can make a hierarchy of what you are afraid of, in which you rank the situations, people, places, or activities that cause you anxiety from least anxiety-provoking to most anxiety-provoking. Then you gradually work your way up the hierarchy—tackling the least feared items on your list until you progress to those items that are more difficult. For example, someone who is afraid of being judged or rejected in social situations may first interact with a store clerk, then ask a stranger for directions, and then make small talk with an acquaintance. Eventually, they could work their way up to calling a friend to make plans, attending a party with strangers, and asking someone for a date.

The downside of using a hierarchy is that it is a slower process and doesn't get you instant results. However, it does allow you to confront your fears at a pace that you can tolerate. Given that exposure work can be uncomfortable, the use of a hierarchy can build your confidence as you progressively confront more challenging situations and teach your brain that there is nothing to fear. If you try to climb to the top of your hierarchy too quickly, then you run the risk of getting too overwhelmed and ending the exposure prematurely, which can reinforce your anxiety and make it worse.

Whether you decide to face your fears by diving right in or using a more gradual hierarchy, exposure can help you get unstuck from anxiety that is holding you back.

YOUR FEAR HIERARCHY

· · · · · ·

To begin facing your fears and evaluating the accuracy of your predictions, follow these steps to create a fear hierarchy.

1. To begin, identify what it is that you fear (e.g., social rejection, driving, flying, insects, animals, bodily sensations, germs, speaking in public, intrusive thoughts, your health). What are you afraid will happen in these situations?

_____

_____

_____

2. Then identify the situations you avoid as a result of this fear (e.g., going to parties, driving on highways, traveling, visiting homes with pets, speaking at meetings, going to the doctor).

_____

_____

_____

3. Now create a hierarchy by identifying 5 to 10 specific situations related to your fear that you could expose yourself to. Rank these situations from least anxiety-provoking to most anxiety-provoking. For example, if your fear involves driving, your hierarchy might look like this:

Least fearful   Drive in the neighborhood

Drive on a main road with one lane

Drive on a main road with two lanes

Drive to the next highway exit at a quiet time

Drive the length of two highway exits at a quiet time

Drive to the next highway exit during a busy time

Drive the length of two highway exits during a busy time

Most fearful   Drive over a highway bridge

Now that you have an idea of what a hierarchy can look like, come up with your own based on your own fear.

Fear: _____

Situations related to your fear:

Least fearful

_____

_____

_____

_____

_____

_____

_____

_____

_____

Most fearful

_____

 LEARNING

You can conquer your fears by facing them head-on. Tackling them from easiest to most challenging might make it easier. The key is to test your predictions and find out if what you are afraid of is actually the threat you are making it out to be.

 PRACTICE

Over the next week, tackle the least anxiety-provoking situation or two on your hierarchy and see if your feared prediction comes true. If the idea of doing exposure work in person seems too threatening, consider bringing someone with you or try doing it in your imagination first.

 COPING REMINDER

• By facing your fears, you can overcome them.

• Exposure may feel difficult and uncomfortable in the moment, but it will be worth it.

REGULARLY REPEAT YOUR EXPOSURE

Now that you've identified your anxiety triggers and created a fear hierarchy, you need to repeat your exposure as often as possible until your fears are eliminated. The goal is to develop new, more accurate conclusions about your feared outcome. In order for this to happen, it is important to stay in the exposure long enough for new learning to occur. Ideally, this may require a duration of 20 minutes, but for some forms of exposure, it may be shorter. The goal is to learn that you can tolerate the anxiety and that it won't last forever. It will eventually subside, so hang in there for as long as possible.

Throughout the duration of the exposure, it's important that you focus your attention on the source of your fear as opposed to distracting yourself. While distractions, like deep breathing and mental exercises, are great anti-anxiety techniques, you want to be as present as possible during the exposure so you can learn the untruth of your predictions. It takes a little time for your brain to process information. Just think about how much time it takes to study for a test. You have to review and rehearse the material several times in order to successfully process this information, and the same goes for facing your fears. In addition, it is rare for something to stick on the first try, so be prepared to do several of the exposures over and over again until you are absolutely convinced that your fear hypothesis is no longer true. You want to ensure that you no longer feel the need to avoid what you were afraid of.

Although you will feel understandably anxious during the exposure, know that this anxiety is temporary. It won't harm you or prevent you from functioning, and it is not a measure of success. Success comes from *doing*— from facing the things you are afraid of—and not from how you feel while you are doing it.

FACE YOUR FEARS

• • • • • • •

To begin facing your fears, select one item from your hierarchy that you can begin doing exposures with. Remember to stay in the exposure for at least 20 minutes, or until you have an opportunity to test your prediction. If self-doubt creeps in during the exposure, remind yourself why it makes sense to do this and take credit for facing your fear. Although the anxiety may feel uncomfortable in the moment, you can tolerate it, and it will pass.

Day/Time	Feared Situation Which item from your hierarchy are you facing?	Feared Prediction What is the bad thing you fear will happen?	Outcome What happened? Did your feared prediction come true?

Day/Time	Feared Situation Which item from your hierarchy are you facing?	Feared Prediction What is the bad thing you fear will happen?	Outcome What happened? Did your feared prediction come true?

LEARNING

Doing exposures gives you an opportunity to test your feared predictions and develop more realistic conclusions. It allows you to realize that the catastrophic outcome you feared most likely didn't come true, allowing your distress to eventually subside.

PRACTICE

Repeat, repeat, repeat! Continue engaging in at least one exposure per day until you negate your fear hypothesis and can move on to the next item in your hierarchy. You want to be able to stretch yourself until you can successfully face your most feared situation. If you're feeling courageous, feel free to move up the hierarchy to your most feared situation or even tackle fears in random order.

COPING REMINDER

- The danger is in your imagination.
- Facing your anxiety gives you all the power.

6

ANGER

UNDERSTANDING ANGER

Anger is an emotion that arises when you feel like you have been wronged or mistreated in some way. Oftentimes, it can arise when you impose expectations, such as your values, priorities, and demands, on the world at large. When these expectations are violated or discredited in some way, you can feel a sense of perceived injustice, and anger erupts. These expectations are typically expressed in the form of imperatives, such as *should, must, ought to,* or *have to.* For example, if your friend is overdue to pick you up, you might think, "They *should* have been here on time." Or if your partner has been spending a lot of time with friends this week, you might think, "They *ought to* spend more time with me." Both instances are likely to result in feelings of anger, which can lead you to act in inappropriate ways because you feel that your sense of anger is morally justified in some way.

However, one problem with demanding that people "should" or "ought to" behave in a certain way is that the world does not operate on imperatives. When you insist that someone call you, show up on time, not cut you off on the road, or wait on you, it does not serve as a guarantee that their behavior will change. Therefore, an important part of learning to manage anger is accepting your powerlessness over the world. The truth is you have no control over how other people think, feel, or behave. By accepting that you cannot control the external world, you can let go of the unrealistic expectation that other people embrace your values, beliefs, and priorities. Instead, you can replace demanding requests with preference statements, such as "It would be nice if…" "I would prefer it if…" "I wish you would…" or "I would like it if…"

REPLACE YOUR DEMAND
WITH A PREFERENCE

• • • • • •

When you have expectations that other people "should," "must," "ought to," or "have to" behave in a certain way, this can cause you to experience anger when these expectations aren't met. One way to reduce feelings of anger is to reframe these demands into a more reasonable preference (e.g., "It would be nice if," "I would prefer," "I would like," or "I wish"). The next time you feel angry, make a note of the demanding expectation connected to that anger, and see if you can reframe it into a more reasonable preference statement. Some examples are provided for you, followed by space for you to fill in examples from your day-to-day life as they arise.

Demand	Preference
You must do me this favor.	I would like it if you did me this favor.
You ought to mind your manners.	I wish you would mind your manners.

LEARNING

Demanding expectations can fuel anger. Replacing imperatives with a preference statement is the first step in dampening down your anger.

 PRACTICE

The next time you feel angry, identify the *should*, *must*, *ought to*, or *have to* that is driving the anger, and try replacing it with a preference. Did your anger or annoyance diminish?

 COPING REMINDER

- Don't should on yourself (or others).

- You are powerless to control how others think, feel, or behave.

- You don't have control over other people, but you *do* have control over yourself.

THE MEANING WE GIVE TO UNMET EXPECTATIONS

Although replacing your demands with a preference statement is sometimes all it takes to diminish anger, more often than not, that only represents the first step to managing your anger. The second step is asking yourself what your unmet demand means to you, or what it means about you. Oftentimes, you'll find that hiding underneath your anger is hurt or fear, which stems from the belief that the unmet demand represented a personal insult or threat. For example, returning to the expectation that your friend "should have been here on time," the underlying meaning that you ascribe to this unfulfilled demand might be "My friend has no consideration for me. I am not important to them." This automatic thought would then drive the feelings of hurt that underlie the anger.

Like any automatic thought, though, you can evaluate your interpretation of the situation using your questioning skills. In particular, you can ask yourself whether the facts support your conclusion. Is there an alternative explanation that is possible? Can you look at the situation another way? Questioning your thoughts often leads to a new perspective. For example, while it is possible that your friend wanted to make you wait and doesn't care about you, more likely than not, they got stuck in traffic, had another pressing issue come up that they needed to address before leaving the house, or just tend to run late.

FIND THE MEANING BEHIND YOUR UNMET EXPECTATIONS

• • • • • •

In order to determine the extent that unmet expectations are driving anger in your life, fill in this worksheet whenever you find yourself getting angry. Identify the demanding statement behind the anger, as well as the meaning you ascribe to the unmet demand, and see if you can replace it with a preference statement. Then question your interpretation of the situation to come up with an alternative view. An example is provided for you first, followed by a blank worksheet you can fill out whenever anger arises in your life.

The Facts (What happened, what you or another person said or did)	Your Expectation (Demand)	Your Interpretation (Meaning)	Replace the Demand (Wish, prefer)	Question the Meaning (Alternative view)
The appliance repair person asked to reschedule after I had already been waiting for three hours.	They should have come within the window they told me to be there.	They don't respect my time. Now I'll have to take more time off work.	I wish they hadn't canceled. At the very least, I wish they had called sooner to let me know they weren't coming.	This was not personal. They likely got held up at another job, or the company messed up. Most likely, they will be able to accommodate what works best for my schedule given the inconvenience I already went through.
	Feelings: Angry Frustrated	**Feelings:** Hurt Anxious		

Find the Meaning Behind Your Unmet Expectations

The Facts (What happened, what you or another person said or did)	Your Expectation (Demand)	Your Interpretation (Meaning)	Replace the Demand (Wish, prefer)	Question the Meaning (Alternative view)
	Feelings:	Feelings:		

LEARNING

Anger is often driven by underlying feelings of hurt or fear, which are associated with the meaning you give to unmet expectations. By evaluating your interpretation of the situation, you can develop a more helpful perspective that decreases your feelings of perceived injustice and overall distress.

PRACTICE

The next time you find yourself getting angry, ask yourself what demand or expectation was not met, including what this unmet demand means to you (or about you). Then evaluate the validity of that interpretation and consider an alternative viewpoint that diminishes your distress.

COPING REMINDER

- Hurt or fear lies below your anger.
- Just because you think it doesn't make it true.
- Beware of giving unmet expectations inaccurate meaning.

DAMPEN THE AROUSAL

When you dwell on the acts of perceived injustice that you believe have been enacted against you, it serves no purpose except to drive distress and block any chance of problem resolution. It also physically taxes your body by activating your stress-response system, which can lead to muscle tension, elevated blood pressure, and overall discomfort. This arousal can interfere with your ability to think clearly, causing you to come to unrealistic assumptions and pushing you to behave in ways you might regret. For example, you might lash out at others or turn to substances as a means to cope.

When you find that your emotions are starting to get the best of you, it's important to step back and take your emotional temperature:

- Red: furious and explosive

- Orange: hot and angry

- Yellow: frustrated and annoyed

- Green: on edge and mildly tense

- Blue: calm and relaxed

If you find that you are in the orange or red zone, that is a signal that you need to take a time-out from the situation so you can dampen the arousal and calm your body. Bringing your emotions down to at least the yellow zone—or even better, the green or blue zone—will allow you to respond more effectively to the situation instead of jumping to conclusions. There are numerous strategies you can choose to calm your emotions:

- Distract yourself by listening to music, counting to 100, preparing a complicated recipe, playing a game on your phone, or watching TV.

- Listen to a guided meditation.

- Pick an object from nature, like a flower, rock, or stone, and focus your attention on it for a minute or two, using your senses to notice as many details of the object as you can.

- Take a walk outside.

- Get some exercise.

- Take a shower or a bath.

- Slowly sip a warm drink.

- Sit in the sun.

- Practice some yoga moves.

In addition, you can try the following progressive muscle relaxation and deep breathing exercises, which are intended to physically relax your body and allow your anger to return to a more manageable level. Once you feel less reactive, you can reapproach the situation with a more level head.

PROGRESSIVE MUSCLE RELAXATION

· · · · · · ·

Progressive muscle relaxation is a strategy you can use to dampen the intensity of your emotions and calm your body. It involves tensing and then relaxing each muscle group in your body, one by one.

To begin, get into a comfortable position, either sitting or lying down, and close your eyes if you'd like. Take a long, slow breath in through your nose, and then release the air out of your mouth, letting the tension leave your body. Now bring your awareness to the top of your head and scrunch your forehead, holding a squint for five seconds. Then release the tension.

Move your attention down toward your mouth and clench your jaw for five seconds, noticing the tension in your face. Then release. Continue moving your awareness down to your shoulders, bringing them toward your ears for five seconds and noticing the discomfort. As you release the tension in your shoulders, notice your body relaxing. Remember to continue breathing slow, even breaths.

Now clench your fists and tighten your bicep for five seconds. Take a nice, slow breath in, and as you exhale, open your fist and notice the tension releasing. Shift your awareness to your chest, holding it tight for five seconds and noticing the discomfort. Then release the tension and allow these muscles to relax. Next, contract your stomach muscles, pulling in your belly button toward your spine, and hold for five seconds. Then release.

Now focus your attention on the muscles in your buttocks, tensing them for five seconds and then releasing. Working your way down into your legs, tighten your thighs by bringing them close together and hold for five seconds. Then release the tension. Next, shift your awareness to the muscles in your calves, holding them tightly for five seconds and then releasing the tension. Finally, move your attention to your feet and curl your toes for five seconds. Then release the tension. When you're done, open your eyes and notice the feeling of relaxation in your body.

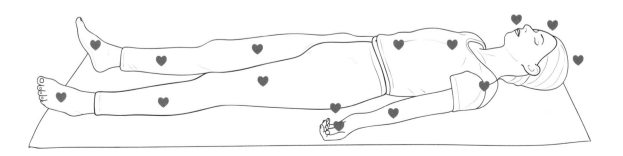

LEARNING

Progressive muscle relaxation is a tool you can use to move from tension to relaxation. It can help shift your emotional thermometer from the red zone to the blue zone, allowing for more clearheaded thinking and less reactive behaviors.

 PRACTICE

Start and end your day by practicing this skill. By practicing progressive muscle relaxation when you are not reactive, it will make it easier to use this skill when your anger is taking you into the red zone.

 COPING REMINDER

- You have the power to calm your mind and body down.

- By relaxing your body, you will be less likely to overreact.

DIAPHRAGMATIC BREATHING

• • • • • •

Diaphragmatic breathing is a simple yet powerful tool that can calm your body down. It lowers blood pressure, raises your threshold for arousal, and makes you less likely to overreact when stimulated. The key to effective diaphragmatic breathing is to breathe as slow and evenly as possible without ever holding your breath.

To begin, sit in a comfortable position and put your hand on your stomach so you can notice the movement of your diaphragm, which should rise with each inhale and fall with each exhale. Then close your mouth and breathe as slowly and evenly as possible in and out through your nose. Try to breathe in for a count of 4–6 seconds and out for a count of 4–6 seconds. The goal is to try for an 8- to 12-second breath. You can either use a clock with a second hand or count internally to keep track of your breathing.

As you continue breathing, try forcing the air into your diaphragm, filling it when you breathe in and emptying it when you breathe out. Continue to diaphragmatically breathe for a minute or two a few times a day.

LEARNING

Diaphragmatic breathing is an effective way to relax your body and raise your arousal threshold, making it less likely that you will overreact to your emotions.

PRACTICE

Try incorporating diaphragmatic breathing into small moments throughout the day. Practice during the commercial break of your favorite television show, when stopped at a red light, or at any moment during the day when your body is revving up.

COPING REMINDER

• Your breath is one of the most powerful tools to calm your body down.

• You can change your breathing to change the way you're feeling.

LOOK OUT FOR PERMISSION-GIVING BELIEFS

Anger is frequently associated with several beliefs—such as "I have to teach them a lesson," "They deserve it," or "They should be punished"—that cause you to morally disengage and mobilize you toward ineffective action. These are known as permission-giving beliefs because they essentially give you the go-ahead to act out on your anger. When you let this happen, you are more prone to lose your temper, seek revenge against those you feel have wronged you, and have violent outbursts.

When you experience these urges to act out on your anger, a good place to intervene is to do a cost-benefit analysis, where you look at the advantages and disadvantages of lashing out versus using an alternate strategy. For example, let's say that you're driving your car, and the person in front of you slams on their breaks at the yellow light. In response, you think, "What a jerk!" and you have the urge to lean on your horn and give them the finger. The advantage of engaging in this behavior is that it might make you feel good in the moment and get the other driver's attention, but realistically that are few benefits beyond this. However, there are several disadvantages of engaging in this behavior. For example, you might start a confrontation with the other driver (and who knows what kind of retaliation might be forthcoming), you could lose focus of your surroundings and hit other innocent drivers, and if other passengers are in your car, then it role models negative behavior and makes you look like a bully.

Alternatively, you could accept the situation and do nothing. The advantage of choosing this alternate strategy is that you won't engage in any actions that come with potential consequences. You are behaving in a way that is consistent with how you'd like others to behave toward you, as well as how you'd like others to treat new drivers in your household or your own senior parents (or grandparents) on the road. This attitude of nonjudgmental acceptance is good for your health and blood pressure, and it makes you a kinder person. However, the obvious downside of choosing this alternate strategy is that you don't get to make your grievance known to the other driver.

By doing a cost-benefit analysis, you can collect all the relevant data and come to the realization that acting out on your anger is usually not the right choice. In turn, you don't let permission-giving beliefs get the best of you.

COST-BENEFIT ANALYSIS OF ANGRY ACTION

· · · · · ·

Use this worksheet to examine the costs and benefits of acting on your anger versus using an alternative strategy. What does the data suggest? Let this evidence guide your decision-making when you are considering taking an aggressive or problematic action.

First, discuss the situation that made you angry.

_____

_____

_____

_____

_____

_____

_____

Next, describe the angry behavior you have the urge to engage in as a result.

_____

_____

_____

_____

_____

_____

_____

Then do a cost-benefit analysis:

	Advantages	Disadvantages
Lashing out		
Using an alternate strategy		

Once you've listed all the advantages and disadvantages of lashing out (versus using an alternate strategy), tally up the number of items in each quadrant. How do the advantages and disadvantages compare? Which behavior makes the most sense?

_____

_____

_____

_____

_____

_____

_____

_____

LEARNING

There is always more than one action you can take in response to anger. When you can look at the advantages and disadvantages of each option, you're better able to choose the behavior that is in the best interest of you and the people around you.

PRACTICE

Before you let your anger lead you down a path of destruction, try wearing the hat of a diplomat and think about how you could negotiate a settlement that gets you what you want without paying too steep of a price.

COPING REMINDER

- Stop and think before you react.
- By not being reactive, you will have more time to be effective.

ASSERTIVE COMMUNICATION

When we're angry, we tend to resort to aggressive communication, in which we speak in a demanding, loud, or threatening manner. This can also include the use of passive-aggression, in which we express our annoyance or dissatisfaction through the use of subtle or indirect jabs. Aggressive communication is ineffective because it typically causes people to respond defensively, which only results in conflict as each party works harder and harder to defend their side.

Another form of ineffective communication is passive communication, which involves not communicating at all and waiting for others to read our minds. When we communicate passively, we don't express our wants, needs, or opinions. Even when we feel like someone has wronged us or taken advantage of us in some way, we don't speak up.

To effectively communicate our needs and maximize the likelihood that these needs will be accommodated, it is important to practice assertive communication. This type of communication leaves little room for dispute, as you simply state the facts in a calm manner, describe what you're thinking and feeling, and communicate what you would like from the situation. With assertive communication, you don't use demanding statements like *should* or *must*, and you're willing to hear the person out and find a reasonable compromise.

TRY ASSERTIVE COMMUNICATION

• • • • • •

In order to effectively communicate your wants and needs in your relationships, try practicing assertive communication. Instead of being demanding or threatening (or being overly passive and quiet), calmly let the other person know how their behavior affected you and express what you would prefer to happen next time. When practicing assertive communication, avoid asking "why" questions, as this will just elicit a bunch of excuses from the other person. Instead, focus on what it is that you need in the situation.

Here is the basic formula for assertive communication:

When _state what happened_ , it made me feel _insert how you feel_ .
Next time, I would like it if _state what you would like_ .

1. What did the other person say or do (or not say or do) that upset you? Avoid using blaming language and just state the facts.

   _____

   _____

   _____

2. Describe how this behavior affected you. How did it make you feel?

   _____

   _____

   _____

3. State what you would like the person to do next time. Be careful not to raise your voice or make demands.

   _____

   _____

   _____

4. Hear the other person out, give them a chance to acknowledge what you just said, and respectfully respond.

_____

_____

_____

5. Be willing to compromise. What do each of you want, and what solution works for both of you?

_____

_____

_____

LEARNING

Raising your voice and being demanding—or staying quiet and not voicing your needs—are both ineffective means of communication because they rarely get what you want (or they get what you want with a steep cost). Assertive communication increases your chances of getting what you want without a price.

PRACTICE

Try using the formula for assertive communication at least once a day. Be clear and direct in how you express yourself. To build these skills, it can be helpful to begin by practicing with smaller requests as opposed to waiting until you're in an emotionally charged situation.

COPING REMINDER

- Being assertive will get you further than being loud.
- Other people can't read your mind.

BREAKING THE DESTRUCTIVE ANGER PATH

Although you've learned a variety of tools that can help you more effectively manage your anger, there may be times when anger gets the best of you and leads you down the path to toxic action. When this happens, it can be easy to fall into the trap of viewing your behavior as a self-perpetuating failure and using it as proof of your shortcomings. However, it is important not to let one mistake define you. You can let this be an experience from which you can learn and make changes. In particular, you can acknowledge your mistake, make amends if possible, and use it as an opportunity to not let it happen again. Instead of letting anger lead you on a path to destruction, use it as a path of understanding and an opportunity to break unhelpful anger patterns. You can interrupt the destructive anger path using the tools you've developed so far by intervening at any of the following steps:

1. Remind yourself that anger comes from unmet demands. Identify the imperative (*should*, *must*, *ought to*, or *have to*) that is driving the anger in your life.

2. Recognize that the world does not operate on imperatives. You are powerless to control others.

3. Replace the imperative with a preference statement, such as *wish*, *like*, *prefer it*, or *would be nice*.

4. Ask yourself what it means to you (or about you) that your demand went unmet. Look for the hurt or fear underneath the anger, as well as the thoughts driving those feelings.

5. Examine the validity of the thoughts that are connected to the hurt or fear. Recognize the answer is not in changing others but in changing how you think.

6. Dampen your arousal by using distraction or relaxation techniques.

7. Question permission-giving ideas to avoid acting out on angry urges.

8. Use a cost-benefit analysis to take appropriate action.

9. Practice assertive communication to communicate your wants and needs.

Each step along this path represents an opportunity for change. Instead of punishing yourself when anger gets the best of you, use it to learn and change. Remember to applaud your success when your anger doesn't get in the way.

URGE CONTROL

URGES

As humans, we all have urges that get the best of us, whether it's eating a dessert we were trying to resist, drinking an extra glass of wine, purchasing something we didn't need, or acting on any behavior we knew was objectively risky. It would be uncommon to find anyone who didn't give in to an urge at some point in time. Here are some common examples where our urges can get the best of us:

- Alcohol

- Tobacco

- Cannabis

- Stimulants

- Hallucinogens

- Opioids

- Prescription medication

- Gambling or betting

- Overeating

- Restrictive eating

- Purging

- Gaming

- Internet usage

- Screen time

- Shopping

- Self-harm

While occasionally acting on certain urges doesn't have to be a problem, it can become a source of concern when it causes you to lose control (or in the case of substance use, interferes with your sobriety). Other urges, like self-harm, are inherently problematic even if you give in to the urge on a single occasion.

ARE YOUR URGES CAUSING PROBLEMS?

• • • • • •

To find out the extent to which your urges are causing problems for you, read through the following statements and indicate whether or not they are true for you.

1. T or F   Acting on your urge has been hazardous (e.g., driving under the influence or going into debt from overspending).

2. T or F   Acting on your urge has caused you to experience conflict in your relationships.

3. T or F   Acting on your urge has caused you to neglect your responsibilities at work, school, or home.

4. T or F   When you don't act on your urge, you feel irritable, restless, fatigued, or on edge.

5. T or F   You have developed a tolerance for your urge, meaning you have to do it more and more frequently.

6. T or F   You find yourself acting on your urge more and more often, even when you don't want to.

7. T or F   You have tried to stop acting on your urge but have been unsuccessful.

8. T or F   You spend a lot of time acting on the urge (e.g., spending all day drinking, gambling, online shopping, or scrolling through social media).

9. T or F   You have skipped or stopped doing activities that are important to you in order to act on your urges instead.

10. T or F   You have a powerful desire to act on your urge that is hard to resist.

If you answered true to two or more of the questions above, your urges are getting the best of you. The more true answers you have, the more your urges are impairing your functioning and causing you distress.

LEARNING

Most of us have urges that get the best of us sometimes. When you yield to your urges more often than you would like, negative consequences result.

. . . .

 PRACTICE

Start recording how many times per day you experience the desire to act out on your urges. Jot down every time an urge occurs, make note of the context, and describe any problems these urges are causing you.

. . . .

 COPING REMINDER

- It is human to give in to urges.
- If there are certain urges you are working to control, know that one slip-up does not define you.

COST-BENEFIT ANALYSIS OF CONTROLLING YOUR URGES

· · · · · ·

Regardless of how frequent or problematic your urges are, it is in your best interest to determine whether it makes sense to work on controlling your urges. If you are not motivated to do so, it can lead you to engage in defiant or avoidant behavior instead of truly putting in the work. Therefore, recognizing the advantages and disadvantages of controlling your urges is the first step. Use this worksheet to conduct a cost-benefit analysis and see what the evidence suggests. An example is provided for you first, followed by a blank template you can fill in.

EXAMPLE:

What is the urge that gets the best of you? *Overeating*

	Advantages	**Disadvantages**
Continuing to act on the urge	1. I don't feel deprived. 2. I like food.	1. My weight keeps increasing. 2. I feel uncomfortably full. 3. I feel bad about myself. 4. I feel out of control. 5. It hurts my health. 6. I waste money on food.
Controlling the urge	1. It will help with weight management. 2. I'll feel better about myself. 3. It will give me time to do other things. 4. My health will improve. 5. I won't spend as much money on food.	1. I might feel deprived. 2. I want to be able to eat whatever I want.

Once you've listed all the advantages and disadvantages of controlling and continuing the urge, tally up the number of items in each quadrant. How do the advantages and disadvantages compare? What does the evidence suggest?

Overeating might have some advantages, but the price of not controlling this urge makes working on it a no-brainer.

YOUR TURN:

What is the urge that gets the best of you? _____

	Advantages	Disadvantages
Continuing to act on the urge		
Controlling the urge		

Once you've listed all the advantages and disadvantages of controlling and continuing the urge, tally up the number of items in each quadrant. How do the advantages and disadvantages compare? What does the evidence suggest?

_____

_____

_____

_____

_____

_____

_____

_____

LEARNING

Often, the advantages of not acting out on your urges far outweigh any possible advantages of giving into them.

PRACTICE

Whenever you feel tempted to act out on an urge, make a list of all the advantages and disadvantages of controlling the urge (versus not controlling it). Draw a conclusion, and use this as motivation to take the steps to regain control.

COPING REMINDER

• Acting on an urge may feel good in the moment, but it's not worth the long-term consequences.

• The advantages of resisting your urges outweigh the advantages of giving in.

TRIGGERS

There are many different types of triggers, both internal and external, that can cause you to experience urges. Internal triggers can include strong feelings (such as boredom, excitement, sadness, or nervousness), body sensations (such as feeling tired or shaky), or thoughts or images that cross your mind. For example, you might have the urge to drink a caffeinated beverage each time you begin to feel the sensations of being sleepy. External triggers can include hearing something on the news, having a dream, or being exposed to particular situations, events, or conversations associated with the urge to use. You may be exposed to these triggers if you walk into a bakery when you are trying not to eat sweets or drink coffee, meet a friend at a bar when you are trying not to drink, or see a targeted advertisement on your social media feed when you are trying to cut back on spending.

Whenever possible, it is preferable to avoid exposing yourself to triggers, as this can prevent you from acting out on unwanted urges. For example, while you cannot avoid food altogether if you are trying to stop overeating, you can avoid the bakery department. Similarly, you can meet your friend at a park instead of the bar if you are trying to cut back on alcohol. However, there are times when avoiding triggers is impossible, particularly when it comes to internal triggers that pop up without warning. In this case, it is important to remember that the triggering thought, feeling, or body sensation will eventually pass. It may feel uncomfortable in that moment, but it won't last forever.

Stress is another trigger that is largely unavoidable in your day-to-day life, but learning to manage stress can help you resist acting out on your urge. Here are some ways to help you manage stress:

- Exercise regularly.

- Practice yoga or meditation.

- Engage in deep breathing or progressive muscle relaxation exercises.

- Tackle to-do lists by setting reasonable goals for yourself with obtainable timelines.

- Accept help from others and be willing to ask for it.

- Have the courage to say no and assertively ask for what you want.

- Make time for leisure activities that bring you joy.

- Keep a gratitude journal.

- Maintain a reliable sleep and wake schedule.

AVOID TRIGGERS BY CHOOSING EFFECTIVE ACTION

· · · · · ·

An effective way to resist urges is to avoid triggers by actively putting obstacles in your path. For example, instead of driving home with a friend who smokes, find an alternative means to get home. Rather than joining a friend at the bar for drinks, invite them to hit the gym with you. Instead of walking into the kitchen to mindlessly snack, head to the shower. Use this worksheet to brainstorm ways you can choose effective actions that help you avoid some of your triggers.

EXAMPLE:

What is an urge you are trying to resist?
Having wine every day after work

What actions will make it easier to yield to the urge?
Checking out the wine selection in the market, stopping on the way home to stock up when I'm out, opening a new bottle of wine

What actions will make it harder to yield to the urge?
Staying away from the wine department, not stopping to replace the wine when I am out, keeping bottles of seltzer on hand instead

YOUR TURN:

What is an urge you are trying to resist?

_____

_____

_____

_____

_____

What actions will make it easier to yield to the urge?

_____

_____

_____

_____

_____

_____

What actions will make it harder to yield to the urge?

_____

_____

_____

_____

_____

LEARNING

When you put obstacles in your path, it makes you less likely to succumb to triggers. Taking effective action prevents urges from winning.

PRACTICE

Take preventive measures by thinking of alternative actions you can take to minimize triggers. Make a list of all the people, places, and things that trigger you, and find alternatives that move you toward effective action.

COPING REMINDER

- You have the power to avoid the people, places, and things associated with trouble.
- Although triggers are everywhere, you can go out of your way to avoid them.

URGE-RELATED BELIEFS

Triggers are so closely connected to your urges because they activate underlying beliefs that perpetuate your vices. This can include beliefs such as "I'm more fun when I'm drunk," "I'll feel better if I eat an entire cake right now," or "Shopping is the only thing that will reduce my stress." When you accept these beliefs as true, they lead to automatic thoughts that make you want to yield to the urges. For example, you might think "I need to drink when I go out with my friends tonight," "I earned this cake," or "I need to buy this outfit." This voice in your head gives you permission to act on your urges, making it more likely that you will give in to your chosen vice.

However, it is important to remember that these beliefs may not be totally true, and most are not true at all. Rather, these beliefs are like a con man who tries to rationalize the urge to use. For example, it is unlikely that you're only fun when intoxicated, that you'll feel better after eating an entire cake (more likely, you'll feel worse), or that shopping is the only feasible form of stress relief. Learning to catch and correct these urge-related beliefs is therefore an important part of reducing your temptation to act on those urges. Instead of thinking, "I need to drink," you can develop a more accurate and balanced view, such as "I might like to drink when I go out tonight, but I don't *have* to have one. My friends like me for who I am." Similarly, instead of thinking, "I earned this cake," you can tell yourself, "While today was very stressful, eating this entire cake is only going to make me feel worse."

RECOGNIZE AND ADDRESS YOUR URGES

• • • • • • •

To start recognizing and addressing the urge-related beliefs associated with your triggers, use the following log to keep track of any urges as they arise in your day-to-day life.

Date/Time	What Urge Did You Have?	What Triggered the Urge?	What Beliefs Did You Have at the Time?	How Did You Respond to the Urge?	What Can You Do Next Time or Tell Yourself Instead?

Date/Time	What Urge Did You Have?	What Triggered the Urge?	What Beliefs Did You Have at the Time?	How Did You Respond to the Urge?	What Can You Do Next Time or Tell Yourself Instead?

LEARNING

Triggers activate urge-related beliefs, which then propel you to give in to your vices. Once you can identify your triggers—and the urge-related beliefs they give rise to—you can develop a more accurate perspective that helps reduce your urges.

PRACTICE

Complete this log at least once a day, trying to catch your triggers and urge-related beliefs as they arise. See if you notice any patterns in how you respond to certain triggers.

COPING REMINDER

• You don't have to yield to the urge for it to subside.
• When you resist acting on your urges, remember how strong and proud you feel.

CRAVINGS

Although cravings are often associated with substance use, they refer to any strong desire to engage in a particular behavior, whether that be overeating, gambling, scrolling through the internet, or drinking. Cravings typically come in waves: rising, plateauing, and then descending. That means that if you resist acting out on a craving, it will eventually pass. While cravings can feel intense in the moment, if you are able to delay acting on the urge—by distracting yourself with a mental or physical activity—it can often help you resist giving in altogether.

Another way to overcome cravings is to replace positive images of your vice with negative ones. For example, instead of picturing yourself contently snacking away on an entire pizza, you can imagine the ensuing stomachache that will result. Or if your vice is excessive alcohol use, you can replace the image of blissful intoxication with a picture of a toilet into which you are vomiting. Similarly, if you struggle with overspending, you can visualize yourself getting a bill for several thousand dollars.

CRAVINGS LOG

• • • • • •

When your cravings are escalating, the key is to act before you give in to the urge. Fight the craving by engaging in a form of distraction (e.g., exercising, calling a friend), using your mental energy on another task (e.g., practicing meditation or deep breathing), or reminding yourself of a time when you did give into the craving and the negative consequences that ensued. By monitoring your cravings and using coping tools when they arise, you can learn that the craving will eventually pass without yielding to it.

Date/Time	What Were You Craving?	Craving Intensity Before Coping (1–10)	Coping Strategy Used	Craving Intensity After Coping (1–10)	Did You Give into the Craving?

LEARNING

Although cravings can feel overwhelming in the moment, when you ride them out, they will eventually plateau and then pass. The sooner you intervene, the easier it will be to keep your craving from getting the best of you.

. . . .

 PRACTICE

Before you even experience a craving, get into the habit of practicing distraction and relaxation techniques so you're better prepared to fight the craving when it does show up.

. . . .

 COPING REMINDER

- Cravings will pass.

- Just because you have a craving doesn't mean that you need to give in.

GETTING UNSTUCK

Learning how to resist your urges is a process rarely accomplished in one try. It takes time and practice to break old habits and establish new ones. Therefore, don't allow lapses to define your character. Instead of judging yourself as a failure every time you give in to an urge, try to view every lapse as an opportunity to learn, correct your mistakes, and solidify your resolve. It is not a sign that you are weak, helpless, powerless, inferior, defective, or undesirable in some way. It just means that you are working through a difficult issue, but this issue is not a reflection of your character and does not define you. Simply because you are struggling with a problem does not mean that you are a problem.

Conversely, you can use the moments when you successfully resist acting on your urges to remind yourself that you are on the right track. Feel proud of the accomplishments you have made and remember those moments the next time your urges show up. Know that with continued time and practice, you can bring this problem under control with the techniques you've learned in this chapter. You can do this and find the wellness you deserve.

8

CONFIDENCE AND WELL-BEING

GROW SELF-CONFIDENCE

In our work together thus far, we have worked to eliminate the self-doubt that negatively colors how you think, feel, and act. Now our work together shifts to helping you grow self-confidence so you can choose effective behaviors that get you where and what you want.

What does being confident really mean? When you are confident, you believe in yourself and recognize that you are a capable, desirable, and worthy person. You recognize your own assets and strengths. You are able to ask for help when you need it, seeking out more knowledge or experience to help you keep growing, and knowing that you won't always have the answer to everything. You also aren't afraid of rejection or negative judgments because at your core, you believe that you are worthwhile. In short, you know that you don't have to be perfect, and regardless of how much you contribute, earn, or do, you are unconditionally worthy.

Fortifying self-confidence is much like strengthening your muscles in that it requires regular practice. You need to take time out of your daily routine to recognize your assets and strengths. You can do this by paying attention to compliments or praise as they arise, reflecting on your achievements, recognizing times when you have helped others, keeping track of your progress toward some goal, and identifying your positive qualities. When self-confidence is in charge, you know that you are capable, desirable, and worthy, which strengthens your belief in your ability to handle life's challenges and to go for what you want.

RECOGNIZE YOUR ASSETS AND STRENGTHS

• • • • • •

To begin appreciating all of your strengths and assets, look through the following list of qualities and circle any that apply to you.

Animal lover	Flexible	Mechanical	Resourceful
Artistic	Foodie	Multilingual	Responsible
Athletic	Friendly	Multitasker	Scientist
Baker	Funny	Musical	Singer
Book smart	Generous	Neat	Smiley
Caring	Happy	Nice	Social
Chef	Hardworking	Open-minded	Spiritual
Considerate	Helpful	Optimist	Sporty
Coordinated	Humble	Organized	Street smart
Creative	Interesting	Outdoorsy	Strong
Curious	Kind	Outgoing	Stylish
Courageous	Knowledgeable	Patient	Talkative
Dancer	Leader	Problem solver	Team player
Detail-oriented	Listener	Physically fit	Theatrical
Determined	Loving	Punctual	Thoughtful
Emotional	Loyal	Put together	Warm
Energetic	Math wiz	Quick reader	Well-spoken
Entrepreneurial	Mature	Reliable	Writer

Are there any more positive qualities you have that come to mind?

_____   _____   _____

_____   _____   _____

_____   _____   _____

_____   _____   _____

LEARNING

We all have strengths and assets that define us—including you.

. . . .

PRACTICE

Whenever things don't go as planned or an obstacle gets in your way, pull out this list and tell yourself "I am _____"—filling in the blank with one positive quality that defines you. Reminding yourself of your assets and strengths is essential to growing self-confidence.

. . . .

COPING REMINDER

- You have so many assets and strengths.
- You are valuable simply by being *you*.

DAILY SELF-CONFIDENCE BUILDER

• • • • • •

To start growing self-confidence, begin collecting and recording data throughout the day that supports a more positive and empowering view of yourself. The validating items do not have to be very significant or official—the small stuff can encourage you too! Be on the lookout for any of the following daily self-confidence builders.

Compliments or positive feedback you received:	Work or social achievements you accomplished:

Stressors or problems you successfully handled:	Responsibilities you took care of:

Kind deeds you did for others:	Invitations you received from friends:

LEARNING

There is often a great deal of external validation that can help you become more self-confident. The key is to recognize it, value it, and use it to remove any doubt.

PRACTICE

Record any validating information you receive throughout the day in this worksheet. Then each night, look at the data you collected and use it to grow your self-confidence.

COPING REMINDER

- If you pay attention, you'll notice that there are countless things you can be proud of.
- Being self-confident is not about the "big" stuff—everything counts.

GIVE YOURSELF CREDIT

• • • • • •

When you don't give yourself credit for all the positive things happening in your life, it becomes difficult to build self-confidence. To begin recognizing your efforts, as well as your accomplishments, follow this list of dos and don'ts.

DON'T:

- Minimize your accomplishments by saying it was "no big deal" or "just luck."
- Focus on the negatives.
- Compare yourself to others. Someone will always be better than you at something, but there are also things that *you'll* be better at than them. Everyone has their own unique strengths.
- Measure success based on outcome instead of effort.

DO:

Record five things from your day that you can give yourself credit for. Even small wins count! Don't discount seemingly minor successes.

1. _____

_____

2. _____

_____

3. _____

_____

4. _____

_____

5. _____

_____

LEARNING

When you can step back and appreciate all your small successes, it builds self-confidence.

 ## PRACTICE

At the end of each day, list all the efforts and accomplishments you can take credit for. Review this list daily, and refer to it whenever doubt tries to creep in.

 ## COPING REMINDER

- Credit is in the doing and not solely in the outcome.
- Celebrate small wins—each step counts and gets you closer to finish line.

WELL-BEING

When you are confident and believe in yourself, it facilitates your ability to take care of yourself. That's because when you can value yourself as a person, you make yourself a priority—this means you will carve in time for your own needs and wants. Instead of focusing all your energy on taking care of others to the point of physical exhaustion, you put yourself first. After all, you can't take care of others if you aren't taking care of yourself. With this knowledge that you matter, you can be fully present in your daily life and experience happiness without guilt.

The components of well-being look different for everyone, but it boils down to making time for yourself to do what you want, with no guilt attached to it. This can involve anything that brings you a sense of relaxation and pleasure, whether that's exercise, mindfulness, yoga, art, dance, bubble baths, spending time with loved ones, sports, reading, or music. It also involves making sure that you are practicing the necessary self-care to support your physical wellness.

Finally, you can enhance well-being by cultivating more gratitude for all that you have in life. While there will always be times of hardship or difficulty, gratitude helps you embrace the positives and wrap yourself in self-love.

MAKING TIME FOR PLEASURE AND RELAXATION

· · · · · ·

A daily dose of joy is essential to your overall well-being. It sends the message that you matter because you are making yourself a priority. Look at the following list and put a check mark by any pleasurable and relaxing activities that you'd like to do during your own time. See how many more ideas you can also come up with.

_____ Ride your bike	_____ Watch the squirrels	_____ Take a walk
_____ Look at the sky	_____ Feel the sun on your face	_____ Practice yoga
_____ Lift weights	_____ Do a workout	_____ Go for a run
_____ Write a poem	_____ Read	_____ Watch a show
_____ Watch a movie	_____ Plan a trip	_____ Draw/paint
_____ Garden	_____ Take a bubble bath	_____ Take a shower
_____ Give yourself a facial	_____ Get a manicure	_____ Get a haircut
_____ Go kayaking	_____ Walk the dog	_____ Go swimming
_____ Go to the park	_____ Surf	_____ Take a drive
_____ Eat a good meal	_____ Cook/bake	_____ Shop
_____ Hike	_____ Call a friend	_____ Meet a friend
_____ Meditate	_____ Shoot hoops	_____ Hit golf balls
_____ Toss a ball around	_____ Play a video game	_____ Swing
_____ Play an instrument	_____ Play a board game	_____ Do a jigsaw puzzle
_____ Do a crossword puzzle	_____ Play a card game	_____ Skateboard
_____ Walk on the beach	_____ Go to a farmers market	_____ Go to a festival
_____ Go to a concert	_____ Visit a neighbor	_____ Visit a relative
Other: _____	Other: _____	Other: _____

LEARNING

There are many things you can do to lift your mood or help you relax. Many of those things are readily available to you at no or minimal cost.

....

 PRACTICE

Try to engage in at least one pleasurable or relaxing activity every day for at least 20 minutes.

....

 COPING REMINDER

- Joy is at your disposal if you reach for it.
- Finding time to do relaxing things validates that you matter.

WELLNESS CHECKLIST

• • • • • •

Use this checklist to remind yourself of all the ways you can insert wellness into your daily life. If you are doing at least half of these items, you are likely practicing the self-care needed to support your well-being, but you can always consider doing more!

Check off all the healthy habits you currently engage in.

_____ I sleep at least seven hours a night (or what is reasonable for my body).

_____ I eat a balanced and nutritious diet.

_____ I regularly exercise.

_____ I go to the doctor when necessary.

_____ I keep up with preventive health care appointments (e.g., dental, bloodwork, mammogram, scans, and scopes).

_____ I set aside time every day to do something just for me.

_____ I make sure to do something pleasant each day.

_____ I make it a point to spend time with people I care about.

_____ I can say no to extra responsibilities.

_____ I can assertively ask for what I want.

_____ I meditate or make time for self-reflection.

_____ I practice yoga.

_____ I sing or dance with abandon.

_____ I take time to reflect on all that I am grateful for in life.

_____ I give myself time for grooming.

_____ I savor my coffee or morning ritual.

_____ I find time to keep up with current events.

_____ I make time to do the chores that matter to me.

_____ I find alone time if I want it.

LEARNING

There are many facets to wellness. What is important is that self-care be a regular part of your day.

 ## PRACTICE

Look for any gaps in the wellness checklist, and make a plan to schedule these components into your day.

 ## COPING REMINDER

- You matter, so take care of you.
- You can only care for others if you care for yourself first.

PRACTICE GRATITUDE

• • • • • •

Gratitude is a powerful tool that can enhance your emotional and physical health. When you practice gratitude, you pay attention to the good things in life, which promotes happiness and overall well-being. In addition, it bolsters self-confidence because all of the positives in your life become more apparent.

To begin incorporating a gratitude practice into your daily life, try any of the following activities:

Keep a gratitude journal and at the end of each day, write down three things you are grateful for. It can be as simple as the warm cup of tea you had in the morning or as great as the appreciation for the roof over your head.

Take a daily gratitude walk outside, where you look up at the sky, raise your arms toward the sun, and savor everything you see, hear, smell, and feel in the environment.

Write a gratitude letter to someone that you would like to thank. Express your appreciation to this person for whatever they did to make your life better, as inconsequential as it may seem. The letter doesn't have to be long, but make sure to be specific about the positive influence they had on you.

Create a gratitude jar. Each day, write down one thing you are grateful for. Whenever you need a wellness pick-me-up, pull out a slip from the jar and read it out loud. Speaking it aloud highlights your awareness of what you appreciate and is a way to honor yourself.

Call a friend, family member, coworker, teammate, or anyone you value and let them know you are grateful for something they have done or said—or just for the fact that they are in your life.

LEARNING

It is difficult to feel confident when you don't recognize the positives in your life. By practicing gratitude, you can develop a greater sense of fulfillment and well-being.

....

 PRACTICE

To make gratitude a daily habit, pick at least one gratitude practice you can do each day and schedule a time to do it.

....

 COPING REMINDER

- You are surrounded by things you can be grateful for, including where you are right now.

- Being grateful wraps you in self-love.

ACKNOWLEDGMENTS

Where to even begin. It's been an amazing 14 years together as writing partners and 27 years as colleagues and best of friends. We initially met at the Beck Institute for Cognitive Behavior Therapy, where Dr. Sokol was the Director of Education and Dr. Fox was a second-year postdoctoral fellow. We are forever grateful to have had the opportunity during this time to have worked directly at Dr. Aaron T. Beck's side. He was a significant force in both of our lives, and we are grateful for all our time with him personally and professionally. His passion, brilliance, kindness, continued curiosity, enthusiasm, and drive made each of us better.

We are so grateful to our families for their unwavering support, especially our husbands, Bob and Stu. You put up with our long hours of writing and weeks at each other's homes and never complained. You picked up the slack with the kids, made us lots of coffee, and waited to have dinner with us. You are both our forever.

We also want to thank our children: Chad, Alex, Max, Jesse, Ethan, and Carly. We are so very proud of all of you and admire your kindness, enthusiasm, smarts, and brilliant help with each project. We so appreciate the fun breaks, help, laughs, and willingness to take our urgent consultation calls. We are in awe watching you become amazing adults.

Thank you to Karsyn Morse for believing in us. We appreciate that you always made yourself available to answer questions and provide us with valuable feedback. You made our passion project a reality. Thank you also to our editor, Jenessa Jackson. You are brilliant, talented, meticulous, and so helpful! We are so grateful to be working with you again! To Alissa Schneider, we appreciate your helpful suggestions in the editing process. Finally, thank you to PESI for giving us this platform.

ABOUT THE AUTHORS

 **Leslie Sokol, PhD,** is a licensed psychologist and internationally recognized leader in the field of cognitive behavioral therapy (CBT), with almost 40 years of experience in practice, teaching, and research. She was a past Director of Education and one of the principal instructors at the internationally acclaimed Beck Institute for Cognitive Behavior Therapy. She is one of the leading CBT speakers in the world, providing teaching and training to professional and paraprofessional groups, both nationally and internationally, on a multitude of CBT topics.

Dr. Sokol is a distinguished founding fellow of the Academy of Cognitive and Behavioral Therapies, was a past president, and is currently Chairman of its Credentialing Committee. She is a fellow of the Association for Behavioral and Cognitive Therapies (ABCT) and President Elect of the International Association of Cognitive Psychotherapy (IACBT). Dr. Sokol also served as Chairman of Behavioral Science for the Mercy Suburban Hospital Family Practice Training Program for over 20 years.

Dr. Sokol has coauthored numerous books and book chapters. Her most recent books include: *The Comprehensive Clinician's Guide to Cognitive Behavioral Therapy*; *Teaching and Supervising Cognitive Behavioral Therapy*; *Think Confident, Be Confident for Teens: A Cognitive Therapy Guide to Overcoming Self-Doubt and Creating Unshakable Self-Esteem*; *Think Confident, Be Confident: A Four-Step Program to Eliminate Doubt and Achieve Lifelong Self-Esteem*; and *The Think Confident, Be Confident Workbook for Teens: Activities to Help You Create Unshakable Self-Confidence and Reach Your Goals*. Her private practice is in Lansdale, Pennsylvania and her website is www.thinkconfidentbeconfident.com.

 **Marci G. Fox, PhD,** is a licensed psychologist specializing in cognitive behavioral therapy (CBT) with teens and adults. She has been in private practice for more than 25 years and worked with the Beck Institute for Cognitive Behavior Therapy for almost the same amount of time. As an Academy of Cognitive and Behavioral Therapies Certified Trainer/Consultant and former Senior Associate and Adjunct Faculty Member at the Beck Institute, she is actively involved in training thousands of mental health professionals nationally to increase their competency in CBT. She has also lectured around the globe on CBT, confidence, and self-esteem. Dr. Fox has founding fellow distinction, as well as invited placement on the board of examiners and credentials committee, with the Academy of Cognitive and Behavioral Therapies. She is also an active member of the credentialing committee of the Academy of Cognitive and Behavioral Therapies.

She has coauthored the books *The Comprehensive Clinician's Guide to Cognitive Behavioral Therapy*; *Teaching and Supervising Cognitive Behavioral Therapy*; *Think Confident, Be Confident for Teens: A Cognitive Therapy Guide to Overcoming Self-Doubt and Creating Unshakable Self-Esteem*; *Think Confident, Be Confident: A Four-Step Program to Eliminate Doubt and Achieve Lifelong Self-Esteem*; and *The Think Confident, Be Confident Workbook for Teens: Activities to Help You Create Unshakable Self-Confidence and Reach Your Goals*.

Dr. Fox has published in peer reviewed journals and has diverse publications in the area of CBT. She has been interviewed for articles in multiple national magazines and on many national and international radio stations. Her practice is in Boca Raton, Florida. For more information, visit her website at www.thinkconfidentbeconfident.com.